Contents

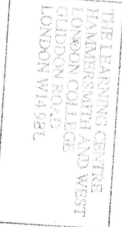

1   **Introduction**

2   **Drugtaking and risktaking**

5   **UK drug laws**

8   **Drug terms**

10   **UK drug jargon**

13   **What's in a drug?**

15   **Basic UK drug statistics**

20   **UK drug treatment**

27   **The drugs**

28   Amphetamines

31   Amyl and butyl nitrite

33   Benzodiazepines

35   Cocaine and crack

39   Opiates

43   Cannabis

47   LSD

49   Hallucinogenic mushrooms

52   Ecstasy

55   Anabolic steroids

57   Alcohol

61   Caffeine

63   Tobacco

66   Solvents

68   Over-the-counter drugs (OTC)

70   **Other drugs**

70   GHB

72   Ketamine

73   Khat

75   2CB

76   Legal highs

78   **Drug group tables**

The Druglink Guide to Drugs

A guide to the non-medical
use of drugs in Britain
(formerly Drug Abuse Briefing)

Published by
DrugScope
32 Loman Street
London SE1 OEE
Tel 0207 928 1211
Fax 0207 928 1771
E-mail: info@drugscope.org.uk
Website: www.drugscope.org.uk

First published 2004

ISBN 1904319165

Design: Andrew Haig Associates

Printed by: Fotodirect

The aim of this booklet is to acquaint the
general reader with the basic facts about drugs
(both legal and illegal) used for non medical
purposes in the UK. DrugScope has a range of
products and services for practitioners and
policymakers. For further information, please
visit our website or contact us for a catalogue.

Enquirers may contact the Information Service
by phone, letter, fax or e-mail. To visit, please
make an appointment first. The library is open
between 10am–4pm Monday–Friday.

Introduction

The use of drugs (including alcohol, tobacco and coffee) for non-medical purposes is an often misunderstood aspect of human behaviour. The most extensive and solid scientific work on drugs focuses on their chemical compositions and effects on laboratory animals. We also know something about the characteristics of people who use large amounts, seek help or get into some kind of trouble with drugs because they are the ones most likely to come to the attention of, for example, doctors, drug agencies and the police, and therefore most accessible to researchers.

But information derived from these areas of research doesn't necessarily help much in understanding the 'everyday' use and misuse of drugs, nor how social and psychological processes influence the outcome of drugtaking behaviour. Instead, it can only offer a very rough guide to whether the consequences will be beneficial or harmful in any individual case.

Drug effects are strongly influenced by the amount taken, how much has been taken before, what the user wants and expects to happen, the surroundings in which they are taken, and the reactions of other people. All these influences are themselves tied up with social and cultural attitudes to, and beliefs about, drugs, as well as more general social conditions. Even the same person will react differently at different times. So it is usually misleading to make simple cause-and-effect statements about drugs, such as 'drug X always causes condition Y'.

The drug-by-drug method of presentation may give the impression that drug users themselves fall into these categories. This is not necessarily the case. While there must be many people who restrict their drug use to alcohol, tobacco, caffeine or cannabis, others (especially compulsive users) will switch drugs depending on availability, or use drugs in combination or one after another.

Under each drug type there is a section headed *Prevalence*. Over the years, the prevalence and relative prevalence of the use of different drugs will change, and drug prices and availability can alter in a period of months. So readers should look upon this section – especially the prices – as accurate for 2004, but only as a guide to the order of magnitude to be expected in the following months and years.

Quotations in this publication are used to illustrate some individual attitudes towards drugs and drugtaking. They are not meant to be representative of usual attitudes or experiences.

The same (or a very similar) drug may be sold under a variety of trade names for medical use. In this publication, trade names begin with a capital, while the chemical name of the drug is in lower case.

> No nation so ancient but had its narcotic soother from the most distant times; none so remote and isolated but has found within its own border a pain-allayer and care-dispeller of native growth; none so savage which instinct has not led to seek for, and successfully to employ, this form of physiological indulgence. The craving for such indulgence and the habit of gratifying it, are little less universal than the desire for ... consuming our common food.
>
> James Johnson, *Chemistry of Common Life*, 1854

Drugtaking and risktaking

The vast majority of people who use drugs come to no physical or psychological harm, and many will feel that they have benefited (and may well have done so) from the relaxation, diversion or temporarily improved social, intellectual or physical performance that can be afforded by some drugs. But there are very serious risks, and a large part of this publication is about these and how they arise. Some of the most important points to be made about the risks of drugtaking apply to all or most of the drugs in this publication. To an extent, these represent rules of thumb about what not to do with drugs in general, though each drug has its own array of potential risks. It should not be assumed that the extent to which a drug is legally restricted is much of a guide to how harmful it can be.

OVERDOING IT

The adage about moderation applies to drugs in two different ways. First, taking too much in one go risks an experience that gets out of control and causes distress or even a fatal overdose. Obviously the more taken, the greater the risk of accidents due to intoxication, including choking on vomit while unconscious.

Secondly, anyone taking a psychoactive drug frequently, in high doses, and for a long time, is likely to experience a distortion in their perception of and response to their environment, such that normal functioning and normal development are impaired. Social relationships may narrow down to a small group of people with similar habits, and finding or keeping work and housing may be difficult. As tolerance/dependence develops, the problems of financing drug purchases can add to the deterioration of diet, housing and lifestyle, and may result in revenue-raising crimes. Normal desires for say food and sex, and reactions to discomfort and pain, may be dulled by the drug, and the resultant self-neglect can damage health. Indirect damage – arising from the lifestyle associated with heavy, and especially, illegal drug use, rather than a direct effect of the drug on the body – is often the most significant, but can sometimes be minimised even if drug use continues. Obviously, heavy use is most likely if someone becomes dependent on the drug, when they will find it hard to stop, despite their health being affected.

WRONG TIME, WRONG PLACE

Even in moderate doses most of the drugs (except the stimulants) impair motor control, reaction time and the ability to maintain attention. These effects can last several hours. No matter how the person feels, they are not as capable as before, and such activities as driving, operating machinery and crossing roads become more hazardous to themselves and to others. They will also be less effective at their job.

Even stimulants may impair delicate skills and the learning of new skills, and in high doses will impair performance of tasks they previously enhanced.

Also many drugs amplify mood, such that if someone is feeling – or is in a situation that makes them feel – depressed, anxious or aggressive, they could make things a lot worse. Even drugs (like alcohol and tranquillisers) we think of as calming people down, can also release aggressive impulses because they weaken the grip of social and personal inhibitions.

INDIVIDUAL DIFFERENCES

Statements about drug effects are often statements about what might happen in extreme cases, or alternatively about what usually happens with most people. But not everyone is 'usual'. For instance, some people develop a toxic reaction to a single cup of coffee, and the normally insignificant elevation of heart rate caused by cannabis can be painful for people suffering from angina pectoris. Glaucoma patients, on the other hand, may find cannabis beneficial, but three strong cups of coffee will aggravate the condition. Individuals with pre-existing psychotic tendencies may be 'pushed over the brink' by their experiences under the influence of powerful hallucinogens like LSD.

Also, the extent to which a drug affects the body tends to vary with body weight, so, in general, less heavy people will get greater effects and consequently greater dangers from the same drug dose than heavier people will. Sex differences in response to psychoactive drugs are poorly researched, but, for instance, it is known that women alcoholics are more susceptible to liver disease than men, due to physiological differences. Individual differences in the degree of response to the same amount of a drug mean that dose levels for a given effect quoted in this publication can only be generalisations.

PREGNANCY

There are several ways in which drugs might damage the foetus. Firstly, heavy use may affect the mother's health either indirectly or, through self-neglect and poor nutrition. Secondly, drugs may indirectly affect the foetus through the mother's bloodstream. Very rarely do they cause malformations; this risk is at its greatest in the first three months of pregnancy.

More significantly, some of the drugs listed in this publication affect the foetus in the same way as they affect adults, and the baby's immature body is less able to cope. Thus drugs like alcohol, opiates, sedatives and tranquillisers, which depress the adult's respiration and other body functions, will also depress these functions in the foetus and in the newborn.

There is also the possibility that babies born to mothers dependent on opiates, sedatives, tranquillisers or alcohol, will need medical care to avoid withdrawal symptoms.

These risks are by no means the same for all drugs, and are best established for drugs with depressant effects. But, in general, heavy drug use in pregnancy is associated – probably for a variety of reasons – with premature birth and low birth-weight, and an increased risk of losing the baby around the time of birth. On the other hand, the evidence on the effects of moderate drug use during pregnancy is generally inconclusive, and many heavy drug users give birth to perfectly healthy babies. But this is an under-researched area, and doctors generally advise pregnant women not to take any drugs if it can be avoided.

INJECTION

Injection of drugs is less widespread than other ways of using them, but also the most hazardous. Drugs that are injected are mainly of three kinds: opiates, sedatives and tranquillisers, and stimulants (amphetamines and cocaine). These may well be mixed to combine their different effects.

When injected into a vein, all the drug enters the blood stream and some is carried directly to the brain, producing a noticeable effect within seconds. For these reasons the onset of the drug's effects (the 'rush') is quicker and more striking after injection. In general, the short-term effects of injected drugs are along the lines

of those taken by mouth, but more intense. Opiates, for instance, produce a sensation of warmth and relief from physical and mental discomfort, but when injected these effects can be magnified into a short-lived burst of intensely pleasurable sensations. Drugs can also be injected under the skin or into muscles, when the effect is more delayed and less intense than with intravenous injection.

The major dangers of injecting are: overdose; infection from non-sterile injection methods (including hepatitis, AIDS and other diseases transmitted by more than one injector sharing the same needle); abscesses and gangrene caused by missing the vein when injecting; and damage from using crushed-up tablets and other dosage forms not meant to be injected.

For a few people the injection may become as important as the effect of the drug, and if no drugs are available almost anything will be injected. Nevertheless, dependence is not inevitable and will take time to develop.

These are just a few examples. But, in general, it cannot be guaranteed that the effects a drug has on an individual will match those cited in briefings like this, especially if that person is particularly vulnerable due to illness or because of their psychological make-up.

ADULTERATION AND MISTAKEN IDENTITY

Drugs offered on the illicit market are not always what they are claimed to be, and if illicitly manufactured they are likely to contain any one of a range of impurities or adulterants. Also, the buyer can rarely be sure how strong the substance is. And even if they did know, they wouldn't necessarily know how much to take.

These factors add greatly to the unpredictability of the effects of, and damage from, the use of drugs obtained without the safeguards of medical supervision or the quality control imposed on licit manufacturers. [*See also* **What's in a drug?**]

DOUBLING UP

People who attempt suicide using large amounts of benzodiazepine tranquillisers almost invariably wake up unharmed. But the same dose on top of a large dose of alcohol could easily prove fatal. This example illustrates the point that effects of drugs which individually depress body functions (alcohol, solvents, sedatives, hypnotics, opiates, tranquillisers) will add up if they are taken together, so that much lower doses of each will be fatally depressant than would normally be the case. Since drugs remain effective for varying periods, often many hours, the two substances don't even have to be taken at the same time.

Doubling up on depressant drugs is probably the most dangerous, but complex interactions can occur between other drugs. Doctors and experienced drugtakers make use of these to 'fine-tune' drug effects, but for most people loading one drug on top of another multiplies the risk of a harmful outcome.

DRUG LAWS

Even the police would agree that most drug offences are never discovered. But to help enforce drug laws police have very wide powers. They can stop and search people in the street on suspicion, search homes on a warrant and remove property, and have successfully used undercover police officers.

The laws themselves are very wide-ranging. An occupier who allows someone to grow cannabis in their house, even if they had nothing more to do with it, has committed a very serious offence. Just planning together to commit a drug offence renders people liable to the same maximum sentence they might have got if they had actually done it.

So even with drugs where the medical dangers seem slight, the legal dangers remain. First-time possession offences rarely attract a prison sentence, but being arrested, prosecuted and convicted, can be enough in themselves to cause great distress and to affect the offender's education or career.

While legal prohibitions help minimise the number of people who take prohibited drugs, the same laws can increase certain risks for those who do take them. Risks associated with adulteration, uncertain purity, poor hygiene, high costs, inadequate or misleading information, possible added delay in seeking medical or social assistance, all these are closely related to the illegality of certain drugtaking behaviours.

UK drug laws

MEDICINES ACT

There are two main statutes regulating the availability of drugs in the UK. The Medicines Act 1968 governs the manufacture and supply of medicinal products (mainly drugs) of all kinds and its enforcement rarely affects the general public. It divides drugs into three categories. The most restricted (Prescription Only) can only be sold (or supplied in 'circumstances corresponding to retail sale') by a pharmacist working from a registered pharmacy, and then only if they have been prescribed by a doctor. The least restricted (General Sales List) can be sold without a prescription by any shop, not just a pharmacy, but even here certain advertising, labelling and production restrictions apply. All the remaining products (Pharmacy Medicines) can be sold without a prescription, but only by a pharmacist.

MISUSE OF DRUGS ACT

The second of the two statutes, the Misuse of Drugs Act 1971, is intended to prevent the non-medical use of certain drugs. For this reason it controls not just medicinal drugs (which will also be in the Medicines Act) but also drugs with no current medical uses. Drugs subject to this Act are known as 'controlled' drugs.

The law defines a series of offences, including unlawful supply, intent to supply, import or export (all these are collectively known as 'trafficking' offences), and unlawful production. The main difference from the Medicines Act is that the Misuse of Drugs Act also prohibits unlawful possession. To enforce this law the police have the special power to stop, detain and search people on 'reasonable suspicion' that they are in possession of a controlled drug.

PENALTIES

Maximum sentences differ according to the nature of the offence – less for possession; more for trafficking, production, or for allowing premises to be used for producing or supplying drugs.

They also vary according to how harmful the drug is thought to be. Class A has the highest penalties (seven years and/or unlimited fine for possession; life and/or fine for production or trafficking). This class includes the more potent of the opioid painkillers, hallucinogens and cocaine. Class B has

lower maximum penalties for possession (five years and/or fine) and includes less potent opioids, strong synthetic stimulants and sedatives. Class C has the lowest penalties (two years and/or fine for possession; five years and/or fine for trafficking) and includes cannabis, tranquillisers, some less potent stimulants, and dextropropoxyphene, a mild opioid analgesic. However, it is proposed to increase the penalties for trafficking Class C drugs to 14 years. Any Class B drug prepared for injection counts as Class A.

Less serious offences are usually dealt with by magistrates' courts, where sentences can't exceed six months and/or £5,000 fine, or three months and/or a fine.

Eighty-five per cent of all drug offenders are convicted of unlawful possession. Although maximum penalties are severe, just over 20% of offenders receive a custodial sentence (even fewer actually go to prison), and nearly three-quarter of fines are £50 or less.

REGULATIONS

Regulations made under the Act divide the controlled drugs up in a different way to take account of the needs of medical practice. In effect they define exceptions to the general prohibitions on possession and supply. The most restricted drugs can only be supplied or possessed for research or other special purposes by people licensed by the Home Office; these drugs are not available for normal medical uses and can't be prescribed by doctors who don't have a licence (e.g. LSD).

> We must hit the criminals who profit from the misery of drug addiction – and hit them hard ... Drug abuse is a disease from which no country and no section of modern society seems immune. It brings ruthless, hardened criminals and weak, self-indulgent users together in a combination which is potentially lethal for good order and civilised values. Stamping it out will be slow and painful... The rewards are great if we succeed – and the price of ultimate failure unthinkable.
>
> Leon Brittan, Home Secretary 1983.

> It (drug misuse) is a worm that is eroding family and community life and creating criminality to feed the drugs. It is a scourge that was on the margins of society only 20 years ago but is now in the centre...We have to get more sophisticated. It is only the beginning of a bigger challenge. It is our domestic war.
>
> David Blunkett, Home Secretary, 2003

All the other drugs are available for normal medical uses. Most are Prescription Only, so they can only be obtained if they've been prescribed by a doctor and supplied by a pharmacy (e.g. strong analgesics like morphine, stimulants like amphetamines or cocaine, tranquillisers and most sedatives).

Some very dilute, non-injectable preparations of controlled drugs – because they are so unlikely to be misused – can be bought over the counter without a prescription, but only from a pharmacy (e.g. some cough medicines and anti-diarrhoea mixtures containing opiates). Medicines available in this way can also legally be possessed by anyone. Additional regulations effectively restrict the ability to prescribe heroin, dipipanone and cocaine for the treatment of addiction to a few specially licensed doctors.

CUSTOMS AND EXCISE ACT

Together with the Misuse of Drugs Act, the Customs and Excise Act penalises unauthorised import or export of controlled drugs. The maximum penalties are the same as for other trafficking offences, except that fines in magistrates' courts can reach three times the value of the drugs seized.

ROAD TRAFFIC ACT

Road traffic legislation makes it an offence to be in charge of a motor vehicle while 'unfit to drive through drink or drugs', and the word 'drugs' here includes prescribed drugs and solvents.

DRUG TRAFFICKING ACT

It is an offence to sell articles for the administration and/or preparation of controlled drugs, for example cocaine kits. The Act also allows for the seizure of assets and income that cannot be shown not to have come from the proceeds of drug trafficking.

ALCOHOL AND TOBACCO

Supply, possession and consumption of alcohol and tobacco is permitted (and permitted to be encouraged) for non-medical purposes, but at the same time availability is affected by taxation and by various laws, many of which are designed especially to discourage young people from drinking or smoking.

SOLVENTS

The Cigarette Lighter Refill (Safety) Regulations 1999 make it an offence to sell gas lighter refills containing butane to persons under 18 years of age. Retailers found guilty of not taking reasonable steps to avoid selling gas lighter refills to under-18s are liable to a maximum of six months' imprisonment or a fine not exceeding £5,000. In Scotland, Common Law provides for an offence of 'recklessly' selling solvents to children.

UNRESTRICTED DRUGS

The availability of some substances containing psychoactive drugs – precisely because they aren't thought of, or manufactured, as drugs – is not subject to specific legal control of any kind. Foremost among these substances are caffeine-containing beverages such as tea and coffee. In certain circumstances, hallucinogenic mushrooms may be used, possessed and supplied without breaking the law. There are no restrictions on the use or possession of 'poppers' – amyl and butyl nitrite – and virtually no restrictions on supply.

> ...policing objectives and public expectations must be realistic. Elimination of drug misuse is generally regarded as an unobtainable goal.
>
> *Drug Misusers and the Criminal Justice System Part II,* ACMD/Home Office, 1994

BEYOND THE LAW

The non-medical use of all drugs is subject to informal 'control' arising from custom and culture and from the requirements of everyday life, though these controls are likely to be most effective with drugs that are a familiar part of the culture. It's no accident that alcohol (a depressant that interferes with performance) is generally reserved for the evening period after work, while coffee and tea (both mild stimulants that can help maintain performance) are made available during working hours. While legal controls aim at preventing all non-medical use of certain drugs, informal controls are probably at least as important in preventing excessive, harmful or inappropriate use of drugs.

Drug terms

Addiction implies that a drug dependency has developed to such an extent that it has serious detrimental effects on the user. They may be chronically intoxicated, have great difficulty stopping the drug use, and be determined to obtain the drug by almost any means. The term addiction is inextricably linked to society's reaction to the user, and so medical experts try to avoid using it, preferring the term dependence instead.

Addict is a drug user whose use causes serious physical, social or psychological problems. As it is a much-abused term, many people prefer to talk of dependent, problem, or chronic drug users instead.

Analgesic is a painkiller.

Benzodiazepines are the most commonly prescribed minor tranquillisers (for daytime anxiety relief) and hypnotics (to promote sleep). They include products such as Valium, Temazepam and Mogadon.

Chaotic use is when an individual is regarded as taking a drug or drugs in a spontaneous way that tends not to follow any typical drug-using pattern. It is generally associated with problematic bouts of heavy use that may cause the user harm.

Controlled drugs in the UK are preparations subject to the Misuse of Drugs Regulations 1985. These drugs are divided into five schedules covering import, export, production, supply, possession, prescribing, and appropriate record keeping. The first schedule deals with drugs such as LSD and ecstasy for which medical prescription is not available. The strictest schedules for prescribed drugs are two and three and these include opioids and stimulants.

Come down is the hangover or after-effect of taking a drug. Reflecting the low feeling experienced after the high of taking a drug, come down is mostly associated with the after-effects of stimulant taking, in particular ecstasy, which can last anything up to four days.

Dependence describes a compulsion to continue taking a drug in order to feel good or to avoid feeling bad. When this is done to avoid physical discomfort or withdrawal, it is known as **physical dependence**; when it has a psychological aspect (the need for stimulation or pleasure, or to escape reality) then it is known as **psychological dependence.**

Depressant is a drug that acts on the central nervous system to suppress neural activity in the brain. Opioids and sedatives are both classes of depressants.

Designer drugs is a term coined in the 1980s to describe drugs specifically synthesised to circumvent regulations on controlled substances. Ecstasy is often cited as a designer drug, but this is incorrect. As an analogue of amphetamine, there was no need for new legislation to control its use when it became popular. In America, Fentanyl, a painkilling drug many more times potent than morphine, induced Parkinson's Disease in some users who sampled it. More recently, the anabolic steroid tetrahydrogestrinone (THG) looks to be another designer drug.

Detoxification is the process by which a user withdraws from the effects of a drug. It usually refers to withdrawal in a safe environment (a detoxification/detox centre), with help on hand to minimise the unpleasant symptoms.

Drug use/misuse/abuse drug use is an easy term to understand. Misuse and abuse are more difficult to pin down, as they are highly subjective. In most circles, misuse means using in a socially unacceptable way. However, the definition currently being adopted defines misuse as using drugs in a way that results in experience of social, psychological, physical or legal problems related to intoxication and/or regular consumption. Many regard the term abuse as too judgemental, as it suggests impropriety regardless of how the drug is being used. In general, abuse means using drugs in a harmful way. As abuse and misuse can be morally 'loaded' terms, many people prefer to talk of drugtaking, or of harmful or problematic use instead, when appropriate.

Flashbacks are hallucinations that occur a long time after a drug (often LSD) has been used.

Hallucinogenic is a drug which induces hallucinations and alters perceptions (e.g. LSD, magic mushrooms). [*See* **Psychedelic**]

Hard drugs usually refer to drugs which are seen to be more dangerous and more likely to cause dependency, such as heroin and crack cocaine, than those designated as 'soft', such as cannabis and LSD. Obviously there is an element of truth in the distinction, but it is generally a value judgement used for propaganda purposes by both pro- and anti-drug lobbies and so is best avoided. The

Drug terms

terms 'hard' and 'soft' when applied to drugs have no legal or pharmacological validity.

Harm reduction is a term that covers activities and services that acknowledge the continued drug use of individuals, but seek to minimise the harm that such behaviour causes.

Legal highs are drugs that do not fall under the Misuse of Drugs Act, although they may be controlled under the Medicines Act. Most are herbal (also called herbal highs) such as ephedrine, yohimbine and salvia, but some, such as poppers, are synthetic or processed. Many are sold as legal and safe alternatives to illegal drugs, but are usually retailed without a licence, and are not without their own risks to health.

Narcotics are commonly used to mean any illicit drug, especially in America. However, the term technically refers to chemicals that induce stupor, coma or insensibility to pain, such as **opiates** or **opioids**.

Opiates are derived from the opium poppy (e.g. morphine, codeine, heroin).

Opioids include both opiates and their synthetic analogues (e.g. methadone, pethidine).

Over-the-counter (OTC) drugs are those which are available from chemists without a prescription (e.g. Benylin, Nurofen).

Overdose (OD) is the use of any drug in such quantities that acute adverse physical or mental effects occur. It can be deliberate or accidental; lethal or non-lethal.

Paraphernalia is the equipment for drugtaking (e.g. silver foil, spoon).

Pharmaceutical drugs are those drugs available from chemists, either on a prescription or **over the counter**.

Polydrug use is the use of more than one drug, often with the intention of enhancing or countering the effects of another drug. Polydrug use, however, may simply occur because the user's preferred drug is unavailable (or too expensive) at the time.

Prescribed drugs are those drugs obtained on a prescription. May refer to methadone and other **opioids** or to **tranquillisers** and **anti-depressants**.

Problem drug use tends to refer to drug use which could be either dependent or recreational. In other words, it is not necessarily the frequency of drug use which is the primary 'problem', but the effects that drugtaking have on the user's life (i.e. they may experience social, financial, psychological, physical or legal problems as a result of their drug use).

Psychedelic was coined in 1956 by the LSD researcher Humphrey Osmond, and literally means 'soul manifesting' – an activation of consciousness. Although virtually synonymous with **hallucinogenic**, psychedelic implies that the drug or experience acts as a catalyst to further feelings and thoughts, and is not merely hallucinatory.

Psychoactive or psychotropic are perhaps the most all-encompassing ways of describing mood-altering drugs in general, though they are more often used to describe LSD and similar hallucinogenic drugs.

Recreational drug use is the use of drugs for pleasure or leisure. The term is often used to denote the use of ecstasy and other 'dance drugs', and implies that drug use has become part of someone's lifestyle (even though they may only take drugs occasionally).

Sedative is a **depressant** which acts on the central nervous system to relieve anxiety and induce calmness/sleep (e.g. **benzodiazepines**).

Stimulant is a drug which acts on the central nervous system to increase neural activity in the brain (e.g. amphetamine, cocaine, caffeine, and – if used in high quantities – **anti-depressants** and certain **opioids**).

Tolerance refers to the way the body gets used to the repeated presence of a drug, meaning that higher doses are needed to maintain the same effect.

Tranquillisers are calming drugs used to manage various mental disorders. They can be differentiated from **sedatives** in that (unless used in high doses) they do not interfere with thought processes or send the user to sleep.

Volatile substances refers to all solvents and inhalants (not, as is sometimes thought, to aerosols only).

Withdrawal is the body's reaction to the sudden absence of a drug to which it has adapted. The effects can be stopped either by taking more of the drug, or by 'cold turkey' – which may last for up to a week.

UK drug jargon

ACMD (Advisory Council on the Misuse of Drugs)

Reports to the Home Office with a statutory responsibility to advise government on the continuing operation of the Misuse of Drugs Act 1971 and changes in the law deemed necessary in the light of emerging evidence.

ACPO (Association of Chief Police Officers)

Police association functioning to support and develop policing. It also has a Drugs Sub-Committee that undertakes research, intelligence work and effectiveness reviews in relation to government strategy.
http://www.acpo.police.uk/

BCS (British Crime Survey)

Home Office-funded research study on self-reported drug use from a large, nationally represented sample of people living in private households in England and Wales. Conducted every two years.
http://www.homeoffice.gov.uk/rds/bcs1.html

CDT (Community Drug Team)

Specialist drug treatment services operating at a local level.

CDRP (Crime and Disorder Reduction Partnership)

The 1998 Crime and Disorder Act established partnerships between the police, local authorities, probation service, health authorities, the voluntary sector, and local residents and businesses. These partnerships are working to reduce crime and disorder in their area. There are currently 376 partnerships in England. To find out more go to:
http://www.crimereduction.gov.uk/partnership.htm

DAT (Drug Action Team)

Multidisciplinary teams drawn from health, social services, education, police and voluntary services backgrounds to lead and co-ordinate local and regional collaboration and ensure coherence in relation to the government strategy. In Scotland, these teams may also deal with alcohol. In Wales, Drug and Alcohol Action teams (DAATs) have been replaced by a new strategic

co-ordination team in each of the four Welsh police authority areas. For more information and access to the main government drugs website, go to:
http://www.drugs.gov.uk/Home

DDUs (Drug Dependency Units)

Specialist drug treatment services attached to hospitals.

DfES (Department for Education and Skills)

Central government department involved in furthering development of, and providing guidance for, teachers, youth workers and other professionals on effective approaches in drug education.
http://www.dfes.gov.uk/index.htm

DH (Department of Health)

Central government department taking responsibility for health aspects of the government's drug strategy.
http://www.doh.gov.uk/

DPAS (Drugs Prevention Advisory Service)

Replaced the Drug Prevention Initiative (DPI) but continues the work of implementing and evaluating drugs prevention action in communities, and disseminating good practice.
http://www.dpas.gov.uk/

DRG (Drug Reference Group – England)

Local organisations advising DATs, DAATs and communities in support of the government strategy.

DAO (Drug Abstinence Order)

An order for those aged 18 or over specifies abstention from using specified Class A drugs (usually heroin, cocaine and/or crack), for a period of between six months and three years, and includes supervision and periodic drug testing of offenders.

DTTO (Drug Treatment and Testing Order)

An order for those aged 16 and over and dependent on drugs like heroin or crack cocaine and who commit multiple crimes to finance their habit. It allows a court, with the offender's consent, to make an order requiring the offender who has a drug problem to undergo treatment for their drug problem rather than being sent to prison.

EATA (European Association for the Treatment of Addiction)

EATA is a membership organisation. Most are voluntary and independent treatment providers, supplying over 50% of community-based residential treatment and much of the country's structured day-care treatment, as well as almost all of the UK's prison-based programmes.
http://www.box-1.freeserve.co.uk/

EIU (Effective Interventions Unit)

The Scottish site which contains a wide range of reviews and reports on 'what works' in preventing and treating drug-related problems. A rapidly expanding site with much high-quality information.
http://www.drugmisuse.isdscotland.org/eiu

EMCDDA (European Monitoring Centre for Drugs and Drug Addiction)

The European Monitoring Centre for Drugs and Drug Addiction aims to provide the European Community and its Member States with 'objective, reliable and comparable information concerning drugs and drug addiction and their consequences'. The EMCDDA works with a number of European bodies and co-ordinates a network of national information centres, one in each Member State (known as 'Focal Points').
http://www.emcdda.org

HO (Home Office)

The Home Secretary has overall responsibility for the national drugs strategy and the department is also responsible for police, prison, Customs and Excise, the implementation of the Misuse of Drugs Act (including the licensing of doctors to prescribe drugs to drug users in support of their addiction) and the Drug Prevention Advisory Service.
http://www.homeoffice.gov.uk/

LEA (Local Education Authority)

A local government authority with responsibility for promoting the government strategy by reflecting drugs education in education development plans and, in some areas, by providing Drug Education Co-ordinators.

LSP (Local Strategic Partnership)

These bring together different parts of the public sector with private business, community and voluntary sectors in local planning. There is no statutory requirement for a local area to set up an LSP, but you can't apply for Neighbourhood Renewal funding unless you have one.

LDAN (London Drug and Alcohol Network)

A London-wide voluntary organisation, set up to give advice, information and support to frontline services – those working directly with people who have drug and alcohol problems in London.
http://www.ldan.org.uk/cms/view/homeguest.asp

LDPF (London Drug Policy Forum)

Established by the Corporation of London and the DPAS to co-ordinate London local authority policy and practice and encourage joint working.
http://www.cityoflondon.gov.uk/our_services/
social_services/ldpf/london_drug_policy_forum.htm

NAC (National Addiction Centre)

A London-based centre for research into clinical practice within the substance misuse field. Also linked to the Maudsley Hospital and Institute of Psychiatry.

NACRO (National Association for the Care and Resettlement of Offenders)

Independent charity providing a resettlement information service for prisoners. It also runs local crime prevention projects.
http://www.nacro.org.uk/

NCIS (National Criminal Intelligence Service)

Collates all types of information on drug trafficking, and for example, monitors suspect movement of precursor

chemicals and associated equipment used in the production of illicit drugs. It develops intelligence on money laundering activities.
http://www.ncis.co.uk/

NCS (National Crime Squad)

National police agency against organised criminals. Broadly speaking, NCS replaced Regional Crime Squads.
http://www.nationalcrimesquad.police.uk/

NTA (National Treatment Agency)

The NTA is a Special Health Authority, established by the government in 2001 to increase the availability, capacity and effectiveness of drug treatment in England.
http://www.nta.nhs.uk/

NDTMS (National Drug Treatment Monitoring System)

NDTMS in England and similar systems in Scotland and Wales provide details on the number of people seeking help for their drug use or associated problems. NDTMS replaced the RDMD (Regional Drug Misuse Databases) in 2001.

NTORS (National Treatment Outcome Research Study)

Department of Health-funded research monitoring the progress of 1,100 drug users in treatment over five years (to 2001) to measure changes in drug use, health, social functioning and criminality. It produces evidence of the effectiveness of four treatment modalities.

QuADS (Quality in Alcohol and Drug Services)

The QuADS Organisational Standards manual offers service providers an assessment tool to improve the quality of services. Many drug and alcohol treatment services use them to carry out self-assessment against these standards.
http://www.drugscope.org.uk/about/
project_hometemplate.asp?id=6

SDF (Scottish Drugs Forum)

The national policy and information agency co-ordinating action on drug issues in Scotland.
http://www.sdf.org.uk/

SRB (Single Regeneration Budget)

SRB provides resources to support regeneration initiatives in England. The types of bid supported differ from place to place and according to local circumstances. They all include some or all of the following objectives: to improve the employment prospects, education and skills of local people; to address social exclusion and improve opportunities for the disadvantaged; promote sustainable regeneration, improve and protect the environment and infrastructure, including housing; support and promote growth in local economies and businesses; reduce crime and drug abuse and improve community safety.
http://www.urban.odpm.gov.uk/programmes/srb

SMAS (Substance Misuse Advisory Service)

Now part of the National Treatment Agency, this was a Department of Health-funded consultancy service and a project of HAS 2000 (Health Advisory Service) aiming to assist health and social care commissioners in England to develop their purchasing and practice in order to improve services. The SMAS commissioning standards still apply.

UNDCP (United Nations Drug Control Programme)

The goal for the UNDCP is to advance and facilitate drug control cooperation to achieve a sustained reduction in the production, trafficking and abuse of drugs. It is responsible for advising governments on drug control matters and for assisting them in developing and implementing national drug control policies and programmes.
http://www.undcp.org/odccp/undcp.html

YOT (Youth Offending Team)

The Youth Offending Team is a multi-agency partnership set up under the direction of the Crime and Disorder Act. The team includes representatives from social services, police, probation, education and health.

What's in a drug?

This is a guide to national patterns and *should not be relied on to determine the content of substances circulating in your area* – only analysis of local samples can do that, and mistaken assumptions could be risky. It is a truism that there is no such thing as quality control in the illicit market. Often the street seller doesn't know the drug content of the goods they offer – so what chance the buyer or the drug service?

Impure street drugs can be dangerous but these dangers are sometimes exaggerated. There is a degree of urban mythology about street drugs – the main one being that drugs are cut with substances such as rat poison, strychnine and brick dust. Such contamination is rare. Unless a dealer has some score to settle, it is not in their best interests to have customers dropping dead from deliberately contaminated drugs.

There is no comprehensive list of what has been added to street drugs. Most drug testing is done for police and customs who only need to identify what (if any) controlled drugs are present. As testing is an expensive business, laboratories are rarely asked for detailed information about other substances.

DRUG CONTENT GUIDELINES

The following is a very rough guide to average purities of street drugs and what they contain. To repeat the warning already given, *this should not be relied on to determine the content of substances actually circulating in your area.*

Amphetamines By a long way, the most impure drug on the market. Typical purity is around 5%, with samples as low as 1% seen recently. The main cutting agents are sugars, followed by caffeine and ephedrine.

Cocaine Anything between 20–90% pure, averaging around 50–60%, with the rest mainly made up of sugars.

Crack Typically 70–75% pure cocaine freebase. Sophisticated production techniques – mainly 'washing' with solvent before or after heating – mean that a high purity drug can be produced from only moderately pure cocaine powder.

Heroin Typically 30–80% pure, averaging around 45–50%, though some samples test as low as 25%. The main adulterant is paracetamol, along with other opiate alkaloids and sometimes methaqualone and diazepam. Sugars, too, are sometimes used to bulk out the product. There is no evidence that heroin is diluted following importation. The average purity of heroin seized by the police is nearly the same as that seized by customs and has been for several years.

Ecstasy Most samples contain MDMA; other related drugs such as MDEA or MDA are now uncommon. Fake ecstasy tablets may contain other substances such as ketamine or amphetamine, although again this is not that common. The average amount of MDMA in a genuine tablet is 70–80 milligrams, but occasionally much larger amounts may be present.

LSD Now rarely seen by police or customs. Usually sold as small paper squares cut from a larger sheet which has been soaked in the drug. Mostly the genuine article, though completely inert fakes are not unknown. Dosage can vary significantly depending, for example, on how the paper sheets have been prepared.

Anabolic steroids Most steroids bought in gymnasia are either fakes or counterfeits. Fakes contain little or no steroid (though sometimes they do contain drugs other than steroid) or a different steroid from that cited on the label. Counterfeits are illicitly manufactured products sold as the genuine pharmaceutical drug.

BATCH TO BATCH VARIATION

Drugs are often cut simply to improve profit margins. But there are a number of other reasons why they may not be as advertised or may vary in content. For example, this week's batch of Mitsubishis (an ecstasy 'brand name') may be of a particular strength or composition; next week's may be entirely different. This could be because there was a supply problem with one or more of the chemicals used to produce the drug ('precursors') so substitutes were used. It could instead (or as well) be due to some error in the manufacturing process, or just that the Mitsubishis of one week have entirely separate origins from next week's batch.

A NOTE ON TERMINOLOGY

Words such as 'adulterant' and 'impurities' are used interchangeably to denote that something other than the pure drug is being sold. There are two main types of impurity. First, substances which are psychoactive but are not the ones the buyer was expecting. Second, substances which are virtually or completely inert. However, these words do have more specific meanings, as follows:

Impurity Substance or substances present in the drug as a natural result of the manufacturing process rather than deliberately added, e.g., opiate alkaloids from the process of refining opium into heroin or the by-products of manufacturing amphetamine.

Adulterants Psychoactive drugs deliberatelyadded to 'mimic' the effects of the drug being offered. This would include the stimulants caffeine and ephedrine that make up much of what is passed off as amphetamine. Invariably this is done to increase profits.

Diluents Inert substances such as sugars (glucose, lactose or mannitol) added both to bulk out the deal and assist the process of dilution for injection.

Excipients Mainly relates to tablet/pill manufacture; the starch or gums used to bind the drug together in tablet form.

In this guide, the word 'impurities' covers all of these.

HOW CAN YOU TELL WHAT IT IS?

Is there any way the drug user can test the drug they have bought or that parents or professionals can get drugs they have found tested?

Field testing kits are available, but they contain dangerous substances like acids. As long as they do so without delay, a parent or worker can take a sample to the police and ask for it to be tested. Some laboratories will test substances at a price, but if the substance *is* a controlled drug then, under certain circumstances, the person who took the drug to the laboratory, and the laboratory analysts, may open themselves up to a successful prosecution for unauthorised possession of the drug.

Basic UK drug statistics

INTRODUCTION

Concerns about drug use in the UK have been rising steadily since the early 1980s and the explosion in heroin use. However, these concerns have not been matched by a reliable set of statistics to enable us to determine just how serious a problem this is. The publication of the government's drug strategy document, *Tackling Drugs to Build a Better Britain*, in April 1998, made it even more important to get a grip on the situation because of the emphasis on the need for evidence-based policies which required more (and more reliable) information. This is beginning to happen but, largely because of the illegal nature of drugtaking, there is still much we don't know and the national picture is one of a jigsaw puzzle with several missing pieces.

Another problem is interpreting the data that we do have. A good example of this are the figures which detail how many drugs have been seized by the police and customs. If the figures for heroin seizures go up, does this mean that the enforcement agencies are doing better than they did last year – or does it mean that there is more heroin about (enforcement agencies not doing so well), so therefore a greater chance that more of it will be seized? It is very difficult to know the answer to this, because, for example, we don't really know the size of the heroin market in the UK against which to judge whether things are getting better or worse. The fact that the price and the purity levels of heroin haven't changed that much in recent years tends to suggest that whatever seizures take place, they don't make much difference to the overall level of availability. And for every dealer or smuggler who gets arrested, there are many others waiting to step into the breach. There are many other gaps in our statistical knowledge; we don't really know how many people use drugs or any particular drug; how many people are waiting for treatment or how many people attend Accident and Emergency Units at the weekend suffering from the effects of drugs.

WHAT ARE THE MAIN STATISTICAL SOURCES OF INFORMATION ON DRUGS IN THE UK?

General population

The best sources of data on people's drug use are the national Crime Surveys. The British Crime Survey (BCS), published by the Home Office, covers England and Wales, with the Scottish and Northern Ireland Crime Surveys (SCS and NICS) covering the rest of the UK.

The BCS is the largest household survey in England and Wales on experiences of crime, including the use of drugs. It has been collecting drug use data since 1982 and provides drugtaking comparisons every two years. The survey only covers those aged 16 to 59 years, so misses drug use among those in their early teens. Also because it is a household survey, it misses out certain groups in society who are heavy drug users (especially of drugs like heroin and crack), such as the homeless and those in prison. But it does report in detail on the main age group of drug users in the UK, those aged 16 to 29 years.

The BCS is useful in providing breakdowns of drug use according to age, region, ethnicity, socio-economic status, drug type and levels of use according to recall periods – such as use in last month, last year and ever (lifetime). All the main illicit drugs are covered.

School students

1 The longest established and largest survey of drugtaking by schoolchildren is conducted bi-annually by the Schools Health Unit (SHEU) in Exeter. The SHEU databanks arise from a large number of independent surveys carried out using the SHEU survey methods across the country, mainly by health authorities in collaboration with other local partners.

2 ESPAD (European School Survey Project on Alcohol and Other Drugs) This is the UK component of a pan-European study (including parts of Eastern Europe) looking at the drinking and drugtaking habits of 15- and 16-year-olds.

3   Scotland and England carry out Annual School Surveys (SS). Both set their national baselines for levels of smoking, drinking and, since 1998 drugtaking among 11- to 15-year-olds in England and 12- to 15- year-olds in Scotland.

Problem drug use

The main source for a measure of problematic drug use is the National Drug Treatment Monitoring System (NDTMS) in England and similar systems in Scotland and Wales. They provide details on the number of people seeking help for their drug use or associated problems.

Drug offences

The Home Office produces an annual bulletin which details the amount and numbers of drugs seized by police and customs, regional breakdowns by police areas, levels of purity, numbers of people arrested for drug offences and what happened to them (fined, imprisoned etc). At the beginning of each calendar year, customs release their own figures for the amount of drugs seized.

WHAT HAVE BEEN THE MAIN TRENDS IN DRUG USE IN THE UK?

From the late 1960s to the early 1980s, drug use in the UK rose steadily, but not spectacularly. The main illegal drugs were cannabis, amphetamines and LSD.

1980s

However, in the 1980s two developments began to change the picture of drug use in the UK. The first was the epidemic of solvent misuse (glue sniffing) among children and those in their early teens. Then, into the UK for the first time, came smokeable heroin and the fashion for 'chasing the dragon'. This new form of heroin meant that the drug could be used without the need for injecting, which previously had limited the numbers of users. It also meant that a younger age group were prepared to experiment with the drug. However, smoking heroin is not cost effective and many found they soon graduated to injecting the drug.

1990s

Towards the end of the 1980s another new drug phenomenon took off – ecstasy. Initially this was confined to those who were part of the early rave scene, but the drug soon became one of the defining features of youth culture in the 1990s. It also seemed to spark a greater acceptance of drug use by young people. This may have been because unlike glue and heroin (regarded by most young people as the drugs for 'losers'), ecstasy was much more 'aspirational', associated with going out to clubs and parties, wearing designer label clothing and so on. Realising that the drug was relatively benign, encouraged young people to try a range of other substances. Some drugs like cannabis came back into fashion, alongside newer drugs like amyl nitrate, GHB and ketamine.

2000s

Cocaine has been present on the drug scene since the 1980s, when it was primarily associated with high earners in the City and among celebrities. The drug still has that cachet, but falling prices have put it within the reach of a far wider range of people, including white collar professionals and those in public sector services. All the key statistics on cocaine use – prevalence, seizures and offenders, and those coming forward for treatment – are on the increase. The figures are similar for crack which, although not as ubiquitous and universally damaging as predicted, has nevertheless caused significant problems in the areas where it has found a level – areas which are not restricted to inner-city landscapes.

As a generalisation, it would seem that the prevalence of drug use in the UK has progressed in a step-wise manner – in other words, a jump in use is followed by a relatively stable period, until the 'next big thing' comes along. In the 1980s it was solvents and heroin, and in the 1990s, ecstasy. Many of the key indicators for drugs appear to be in a stable mode at the moment. It might be that cocaine is actually the 'next big thing', although it appears to be growing by stealth rather than by explosion. There is also a realisation that polydrug use (which has probably always been the normal mode of consumption within the drug culture) is a specific problem which needs to be addressed.

Basic UK drug statistics

WHAT ARE THE MOST POPULAR ILLEGAL DRUGS? HOW MANY PEOPLE USE DRUGS?

Key findings from the 2001/02 British Crime Survey for the 16–24 and 16–59 age ranges reveal the following figures for having used in the past year and the past month:

Drug and time period	16–24 as %	Estimated numbers last year	16–59 as %	Estimated numbers last year
Cannabis		1.4–1.6m		3.1–3.4m
Last year	26.9		10.6	
Last month	17.1		6.6	
Ecstasy		334–440k		609–760k
Last year	6.8		2.2	
Last month	3.6		1.1	
Amphetamines		240–332k		432–561k
Last year	5.0		1.6	
Last month	2.0		0.7	
Cocaine		234–324k		553–698k
Last year	4.9		2.0	
Last month	2.1		0.9	
Amyl nitrite (poppers)		178–258k		326–439k
Last year	3.8		1.2	
Last month	1.5		0.6	
Magic mushrooms		63–114k		119–191k
Last year	1.5		0.5	
Last month	0.5		0.2	
LSD		49–95k		84–146k
Last year	1.2		0.4	
Last month	0.3		0.1	
Tranquillisers		38–80k		134–210k
Last year	1.0		0.5	
Last month	0.3		0.2	
Glues		21–54k		29–69k
Last year	0.6		0.1	
Last month	0.2		0.1	
Crack		15–45k		39–85k
Last year	0.5		0.2	
Last month	0.1		0.1	
Heroin		9–34k		32–73k
Last year	0.3		0.2	
Last month	0.2		0.1	
Anabolic steroids		5–26k		12–42k
Last year	0.2		0.1	
Last month	0.1		–	
Methadone		–		12–41k
Last year	–		0.1	
Last month	–		0.1	
Any drug		1.5–1.7m		3.5m–3.9m
Last month	18.8		7.5	
Last year	29.6		12.0	

HOW MANY PEOPLE ARE IN TREATMENT FOR DRUG PROBLEMS?

Up until 1996, any doctor treating someone for an addiction to opiates or cocaine, or who they believed to be addicted, was obliged to notify the Home Office who kept a register – called the Addicts Index – for statistical purposes. Doctors could also phone in to check if their patient was simultaneously receiving treatment from another doctor. When the Index was discontinued, there were about 37,000 people on the Index. Reporting is now the responsibility of the Department of Health and the figure they calculated from returns from treatment agencies in 2000/01 was 118,000. The latest provisional figure is 127,000. The significant increases from 1996 are likely to be through increasing numbers of people coming forward, although the absolute numbers of those with primarily heroin problems may also be on the rise.

HOW MANY PROBLEM DRUG USERS ARE THERE?

This is very hard to determine, not least because there is no clear definition of what a problem drug user is or what drugs this definition covers. But let us assume that those with the *most* problems are likely to be addicted to heroin and/or crack. Back in the 1980s, it was estimated from research that for every one person who came forward for treatment, there were five chronic drug users who did not. The figure was revised down to 1:3 when the advent of HIV/AIDS meant that more methadone was being prescribed for longer periods. Taking that figure would mean that in 1995, there were around 120,000 problem drug users in the UK. The lowest current estimate in the updated drug strategy is 250,000, but recent Home Office research conducted by York University indicated a range of 280,000–500,000. If the 1:3 figure still holds, then based on the latest estimate of 127,000 people in treatment, this would put the heroin using population at around 380,000.

HOW MANY PEOPLE DIE FROM USING DRUGS?

Official data are held by the Office for National

Statistics (ONS) and the General Register Offices (GRO) for Scotland and Northern Ireland. The first two established special databases on drug-related deaths several years ago. All the data come from death certificates, supplemented by information from coroners following inquests or, in the case of Scotland, from pathologists. The National Programme on Substance Abuse Deaths (np-SAD), based in the Department of Addictive Behaviour & Psychological Medicine at St George's Hospital Medical School, receives data on a voluntary basis on drug-related deaths from most coroners in England and Wales. Recently, they have started to receive data from coroners in Northern Ireland and their Scottish equivalents (procurators fiscal). There is also the annual survey of volatile substances (solvent) deaths collated by the Department of Public Health Sciences at St George's Hospital Medical School.

Drug-related deaths in England and Wales 1996 to 2001

Cocaine	338
Amphetamine	390
Ecstasy	161
Heroin/Morphine	4,126
Methadone	1,896
Temazepam	525
Solvents	309 (1996–2000)
Alcohol	200,000 to 400,000 approx.
Tobacco	one million plus approx.

HOW MANY DRUG OFFENDERS ARE THERE?

In 2000, a total of 103,540 people were convicted of a drug offence. Of those:

- 93,000 were male
- 10,000 were female
- Average age of offenders was 25 years old
- Nearly 22,000 of those convicted were under the age of 21
- Nearly 90% of these offences were for possession of which over 75% were for cannabis

Basic UK drug statistics

HOW MANY DRUGS ARE SEIZED BY POLICE AND CUSTOMS?

Number of drug seizures and quantity seized by Class and drug type, United Kingdom, 1991–2001

Drug class and type	1991	1997	1998	1999	2000	2001
Class A						
Cocaine	1446	3837	5209	5858	6005	6984
Crack	583	1684	2488	2507	2765	3688
Heroin	2640	12508	15152	15519	16457	18168
LSD	1636	852	623	480	297	168
Ecstasy-type	1735	5098	4850	6637	9784	10411
Methadone	427	1573	1584	1215	1171	1072
All Class A	8504	24791	28801	30917	34510	37915
Class B						
Amphetamines	6821	18609	18630	13393	7073	6799
Cannabis (herbal)	7515	29409	32592	27092	28321	32498
Cannabis plants	1045	3791	2832	2288	2038	1875
Cannabis resin	52903	79601	84983	73764	65405	63748
All Class B	63715	120031	127693	108332	96495	98954
Class C						
Benzodiazepines (excluding Temazepam)	483	1700	2058	1924	1497	1668
Temazepam	NA	720	913	552	354	452
Anabolic steroids	NA	154	171	106	91	141
All Class C	857	2634	3130	2593	1957	2299
Total drug seizures	69807	139874	151749	134101	125079	130894
Class A						
Cocaine	1075.8	2350.2	2961.6	2960.5	3947.8	2841.8
Crack	1.8	33.5	25.5	16.4	25.5	55.7
Heroin	492.8	2235.0	1348.1	2346.3	3386.4	3929.0
LSD[1]	98.9	158.0	37.5	68.4	25.4	9.4
Ecstasy-type[1]	420.7	2029.0	2127.3	6329.6	6552.2	7668.4
Methadone	0.7	117.3	82.5	64.1	110.4	114.6
Class B						
Amphetamines	420.6	3296.3	1810.8	2019.2	1744.5	1716.6
Cannabis (herbal)	9524.6	31120.2	21729.5	15885.3	25489.8	26741.0
Cannabis plants[2]	8896	115057	123043	55810	47947	71507
Cannabis resin	22663.0	118854.3	88522.3	53044.7	48366.3	58996.8
Class C						
Benzodiazepines (excluding Temazepam)	0.7	2.2	2.9[3]	7.3	3.1	11.4[5]
Temazepam	NA	4.0	59.2	1.2	0.8	1.1[6]
Anabolic steroids	NA	455.5	17.6[4]	73.8	47.3	71.8[7]

Notes: the total number of seizures is less than the total for the three drug categories as seizures involving more than one drug are counted as a single seizure but are counted separately against each individual drug or drug class involved, and some drug types are not shown.
1 Thousands of doses/tablets
2 Number of plants
3 510,345 tablets were also seized by Customs
4 94,583 ampoules were also seized by Customs
5 50,180 tablets were also seized by Customs
6 55,333 doses were also seized by Customs
7 11,629 doses/tablets were also seized by Customs

UK drug treatment

GETTING ADVICE AND TREATMENT

If somebody needs help with a drug problem, there are various routes into advice and treatment available in the UK. Users can access these services either, through the health and welfare system (e.g. via a drugs advice service or GP referral) or, through the criminal justice system. The National Treatment Agency has introduced a Models of Care framework to ensure that there is consistency and equity in the provision of drug services across the country. This framework provides a tier of types of drug treatment services, classified in a way that is easy to understand. The framework also means that the individual can choose from a range of services available to them, and that they can move through the tiers according to their needs.

HEALTH AND WELFARE SYSTEM

GPs

Problem drug users invariably experience physical and psychological difficulties, and in most cases, the main source of primary care will be their local doctor. GPs can refer patients on to treatment services, as well as provide general medical services, promote harm minimisation and participate in an overall treatment regime in partnership with the local DDU or CDT in an arrangement known as shared care.

Street agencies

Street agencies provide advice, sterile needles and syringes, counselling, supervised detoxification and other therapies, such as yoga and acupuncture. Usually they are open only during normal working hours, but appointments are not necessary.

Drug dependency units (DDUs)

DDUs are usually located in, or adjacent to, hospitals. They will see users without a referral, but not without an appointment. Waiting lists can be long, although this is improving in many areas. DDUs provide counselling, detoxification, substitute prescribing and other related therapies.

Community drug teams (CDTs)

They offer similar multi-disciplinary services as DDUs, and, as their name suggests, they are often located in the community.

Outreach services

Outreach attempts to bring the service to the user by offering individual advice, support and risk-reduction interventions, such as providing clean injecting equipment and condoms to those who would not normally come in contact with services. Outreach also offers peer-type education to encourage lower-risk behaviour.

The service comes in two forms: detached work, where workers go out into the users' own environment such as raves and homes; and institutional work, where the service works on site with other agencies such as health centres and schools. Many of the institutional outreach projects do have a close relationship with some agencies and are able to put individuals in touch with appropriate helpers.

Residential services

Residential-treatment programmes are used by heavily dependent users who experience on-going social and psychological problems, such as a disturbed family life, homelessness and engage in persistent criminal activities.

Residents must be drug free on admission, which usually entails that the entrant has undergone detoxification before entry, although some programmes provide this facility on admission. Programmes usually last three to six months, with some 12-step programmes lasting 12 months. These services are usually found in rural settings, often with a large catchment area. At present there are around 2,000 residential places in the UK.

Programmes vary widely in concept and practice, but fall into four main categories:

Therapeutic communities

They operate a hierarchical structure and residents work their way through it as part of the programme. The structure consists of intense therapy sessions involving all members of the community on an equal basis.

UK drug treatment

TIERS OF DRUG TREATMENT PROVISIONS

Tier	Type	Service
1	Non-specific (general)	General Practitioners (General Medical Services) Probation Housing
2	Open access	Advice & Information Drop-in service Harm reduction services
3	Community services	Community Drug Teams Drug Dependency Units Day Treatment
4a	Specialist services (residential)	In-patient Residential rehabilitation
4b	Highly specialist (non-substance misuse)	Liver units Forensic services

Minnesota model

Associated with the Alcoholics/Narcotics Anonymous programmes, the Minnesota model offers a 12-step programme towards long-term abstinence. Based on the idea that addiction is a disease, and devised by the Hazelden Hospital in Minnesota, the programme offers spiritual as well as practical guidance. A number of programmes offer detoxification on entry, and many may require a financial contribution from the resident or their family, according to their disposable income.

General house

As the term implies, these programmes differ from one another in their approach. All provide group and individual support. Participants are encouraged to take an active role in monitoring and shaping their therapy.

Christian house

The programme may be run by Christian, or non-Christian, staff, with, or without, any required religious structure. Where there is a specific religious requirement, non-Christian, and gay/lesbian people will not be accepted. Those without a required religious structure, but run by Christian staff, offer group and individual support, and encourage participants to monitor and shape their therapy.

Helplines

There are an increasing number of helplines available to drug users, which offer confidential advice on HIV, alcohol dependence, drug misuse, drug awareness, general information and counselling. The main one for drugs is **Talk to Frank** (Tel. 0800 776600) which offers free, confidential information and advice 24 hours a day and is part of the government's overall public information campaign to encourage people to come forward for help. Others include **Drinkline** (Tel. 0800 917 8282), which offers a similar service for alcohol.

Self help groups

Narcotics Anonymous and **Families Anonymous** provide advice and support to the user or their families, and provide a self-help regime, usually a 12-step abstinence model. Other services offer participation in self-help groups and counselling sessions; **ADFAM** for example provides information about such groups and supervise counselling.

CRIMINAL JUSTICE SYSTEM

In April 2003, the government launched the Criminal Justice Intervention Programme (CJIP), under the banner 'Out of crime and into treatment'. This programme builds on existing provisions for referral to treatment, and treatment itself, within the criminal justice system, but adopts more of a case management approach which tries to ensure that offenders with chronic drug problems are cared for through the system and, crucially, into aftercare services covering the following areas:

- Police custody

- The courts and probation

- Prison

- Treatment

- Throughcare and aftercare

The new elements of CJIP cover:

- Enhanced Arrest Referral of drug-misusing offenders into treatment by drug workers in custody suites. This adds a case management element and other 'best practice' to the schemes started by the police in recent years.

- Changes in legislation to extend procedures to the under-18s.

- Drug testing, for cocaine and opiates, for offenders charged with 'trigger' offences.

- Community sentences with treatment conditions (such as Drug Treatment and Testing Orders) attached – to be more widely used and supported by all the agencies to make sure they are effective.

- Counselling, Assessment, Referral, Advice and Throughcare (CARAT) service in prisons, including treatment programmes – to be integrated into the way drug-misusing offenders are managed by multi-agency teams.

Some of the CJIP elements in more detail are:

Police

Arrest referral schemes, introduced in 1996, take advantage of the regular contact made with drug users, to encourage them to seek support. This can range from the offer of contact numbers, to getting access to on-site drug workers. Most schemes do not require those being approached to take up treatment, and although take up rates appear to be low for the whole scheme (around 25% of those approached), those who have accepted treatment appear to benefit from their referral, with proportions reporting heroin- and/or crack cocaine- use halved.

Prisons

One of the key objectives of the Prison Drug Strategy is to make drug services within the system more accessible, reflecting more closely the range of services available on the outside. Prisons, therefore, are required to provide a set standard of care, and reduce the harm caused by drug use.

Available to the user within the system are a range of in-house treatment services, advice, information and harm minimisation provisions (at the moment, however, clean needles are not provided, although some prisons provide sterilisation facilities). Prison doctors are able to refer prisoners on to services, which are provided either in-house or by institutional workers. In the majority of these cases take up of treatment is voluntary. However, the introduction of drug-treatment orders and mandatory drug testing has meant that prisoners can be required to take up treatment within the system or on probation. Here individuals have to present themselves for assessment and take up a prescribed treatment regime.

Drug Treatment and Testing Orders (DTTOs)

DTTOs aim to break the link between problematic drug use and crime by supervising offenders with drug problems, and implementing and monitoring drug treatment under sentence. Under a DTTO, an offender is required to undertake treatment to reduce or eliminate their drug use as part of their community sentencing. Lasting from six months to three years, DTTOs can involve a range of treatments, including residential and detoxification. DTTOs require the consent of the offender. Although similar to probation orders 1A(6), DTTOs differ in three ways. Firstly, courts retain the sentence throughout its length by holding regular reviews. Secondly, regular or random urine tests are administered to monitor progress. Thirdly, changes to sentencing are permitted in response to progress or problems.

CARATS

The provision of help and throughcare of prisoners is founded in all prisons on the CARATS framework (Counselling, Assessment, Referral, Advice and Throughcare Services). The scheme provides low-level

UK drug treatment

intervention for prisoners with low to moderate drug problems and aims to:

- identify (problem) drug users as soon as possible;

- provide ongoing support and advice while in prison;

- assess, and engage prisoners in appropriate help where needed, in partnership with internal and external agencies;

- link various departments and agencies involved in dealing with prisoners, including prison officers, medical staff, psychologists, specialist drug workers and probation officers to create the CARATS team;

- provide continuity between treatment in prison and that available on release.

Entrance into a CARATS scheme can occur at any stage of a sentence or remand. Prisoners can self-refer, although most are referred following a reception interview, a medical assessment, or a positive Mandatory Drugs Test (regular mandatory tests carried out on inmates to screen for drug use). Care is generally overseen by the prison's drugs strategy co-ordinator. Direct care and care planning is undertaken by an allocated CARATS worker, who will meet, assess and monitor the progress of the prisoner. Probation officers take the lead role in throughcare arrangements.

Probation

The core of probation work is to prevent individuals from re-offending, and part of that work is to minimise the problems caused by drug use. Probation services have good contacts with local health authorities and street agencies and can refer individuals to appropriate services and treatment. They also play an important role in supervising care and reporting to courts prior and after sentencing; overseeing the management of care and the participation of the user; and providing information and support in the form of housing and benefits. Throughcare may also be available. Here the individual has the right to ensure from the prison and probation service the continuation of treatment by retaining contact with outside agencies and close family, and, importantly, making provision for care and treatment upon release.

DIFFERENT TYPES OF TREATMENT

Once in the treatment system, the following represents, briefly, the main types of intervention available in the UK.

Advice and Counselling

Intervention can range from individual therapy to counselling, as well as advice in arranging suitable housing, work and benefits. Almost all street agencies and DDUs offer counselling as part of their remit to provide support to problem users.

Opiate (detox) detoxification

The aim of detox is to eliminate the drug, usually heroin, from the body, prior to some form of extended support to help maintain abstinence. Doses of the drug, or a substitute, such as methadone or lofexedine in the case of heroin, are gradually reduced over time, or abruptly stopped, until the user is drug free, often using other drugs including substitute drugs to alleviate several of the withdrawal symptoms. Treatment continues until symptoms, or drug use, have ceased. Detox programmes can be administered on an in-patient basis usually in psychiatric units or medical wards, or on a community basis, provided on the NHS by Drug Dependency Units (DDU), Community Drug Teams (CDTs) or by private clinics (some of which take NHS clients). Individuals are usually referred to such clinics either by GPs or drug agencies. On completion of detox, support is provided by CDTs, day programmes and outpatient services.

Methadone reduction programmes

Methadone reduction programmes involve the prescribing of methadone to opiate users to control withdrawal symptoms. The aim is to gradually reduce the quantity prescribed until the user experiences no withdrawal complaints and is drug free. The degree of reduction and length of time afforded to achieve abstinence can vary greatly from a few weeks to several months, depending on the requirements of the individual. Motivation is often seen as a key issue in such programmes. Participants are regularly asked to review their progress (e.g. weekly), whilst receiving therapy and support as part of a structured methadone programme. Methadone reduction programmes are delivered in a community setting, with care from nursing staff and doctors. Pharmacies are the main suppliers of the drug and often supervise consumption.

Methadone maintenance programme

In this case the aim of the programme is not to eliminate drug use in the short term, but to stabilise the user by prescribing methadone as a substitute for heroin and other opiates – therefore reducing illicit drug use, the need for criminal activity and the harm caused by injecting. The programmes are delivered in a community setting and may be structured, as with reduction programmes. The methadone is either supplied by a pharmacy or by specialist drug clinics where consumption is usually supervised. As a general rule, more complex users – that is those with more chaotic lifestyles and problematic use, are treated by drug clinics which provide more support and supervision. Less chaotic users tend to be seen by CDTs who provide structured and supervised off-site dispensing, while those in a more stable situation will be prescribed methadone by their GP, to use, unsupervised, at home. It is not uncommon for a user to be prescribed the drug for several months or years.

Concerns have been raised that increasing amounts of methadone are leaking into the illicit market, often sold to buy heroin. This leakage into the illicit market has, it is thought, led to an increase in the number of methadone-related deaths over the last few years. Guidelines for the prescribing of drugs to problem drug users are provided by the Department of Health and the National Treatment Agency

However, there is also concern that users are routinely prescribed amounts insufficient for their needs, with the consequence that many seek heroin to boost their existing methadone use.

Heroin prescribing

Because of the well-publicised activities of a few doctors, there is a mistaken belief that (diamorphine) heroin prescribing is an established part of the current UK treatment policy. Very few doctors are licensed to prescribe heroin to addicts. Currently only 450 people are prescribed diamorphine, although this number may change as a result of renewed interest in this therapy

following trials in Switzerland and the Netherlands. The National Treatment Agency and the Joseph Rowntree Foundation have published reports on heroin prescribing.

Treatment for stimulant drug use

Although legally permissible, the issue of prescribing the drug of choice for amphetamine users is a contentious one. On the one hand, advocates of prescribed amphetamine argue that, in extreme cases, short-term maintenance is effective as a means of rapid stabilisation. On the other hand, GPs and drug agencies highlight the risks associated with continued amphetamine use and its inherent psychological and physical consequences.

Most agencies offer some form of limited amphetamine treatment such as counselling, referral to residential rehabilitation and ameliorative prescribing regimes, alternative therapies such as acupuncture, relapse prevention and stress management techniques with alternative (not substitute) prescriptions – usually antidepressants. Structured day programmes are available.

The lack of specialist care also applies to those dependent on cocaine and crack. However, over the last decade, due to concerns about the increase of crack use, agencies have responded by offering more specialised treatment for this group including counselling, cognitive behavioural therapy, and acupuncture and other complementary therapies. Unlike amphetamine, the prescribing of cocaine to a chronic drug user does require a Home Office licence. Thus the only drug treatment likely to be offered to this type of user would be antidepressants. There are a number of support groups for female crack users.

Services for young people

Most services are ill equipped to deal with needs of young people (defined as anyone under the age of 18). Services for young people should operate within the Children Act 1989, which entails partnership work with local Area Child Protection Committees and social services children and families teams, along with other relevant child-focussed agencies. The parents or guardians of the young person should also be involved where possible, although treatment may be provided

UK drug treatment

without parental consent in certain situations. Unlike services for adults, treatment services for young people are not able to provide a fully confidential service, as sharing information with social services may be good practice in certain child protection situations. Other young people's services, such as needle exchanges, may not be provided without full assessment and further intervention where possible.

Other developments are currently leading towards integrated children's services that are able to address multiple needs and vulnerabilities. Children's Service Plans will encompass various coexisting service plans, such as a youth justice plan or a drug action plan. The Connexions Service provides a personal adviser for every young person aged 13–19 who will broker access to services and liaise with schools, parents and primary and other carers.

The drugs

Amphetamines

Amphetamines are synthetic stimulants similar in structure to norepinephrine, a naturally occurring chemical in the brain. There are three types of amphetamine, the strongest being methylamphetamine, followed by dexamphetamine, and then laevo- or d'l-amphetamine. Amphetamines are legitimately sold as powders or tablets under names such as Dexedrine (dexamphetamine sulphate) and Ritalin (methylphenidate hydrochloride).

Amphetamine sulphate or speed, the name given to illicitly produced amphetamine, is usually a mixture of d'l-amphetamine and dexamphetamine, cut to a retail strength of around 10 to 12%. Adulterants include caffeine, glucose powder and sometimes chalk.

Amphetamine-like drugs include less potent stimulants such Phentermine and others like fenfluramine which have been withdrawn across Europe because of their association with heart problems.

Relatively recent newcomers on the amphetamine scene are two potent versions of the drug. Amphetamine base, which usually comes as a paste, is a form the drug takes during manufacture previous to being crystallised into a powder. Smoked or swallowed base can be 50% or more pure amphetamine. An import from the USA is methylamphetamine (or methamphetamine as it is known in the US). In its crystalline form, it is known as Ice, a smokeable or injectable form of amphetamine powder, similar in its relation to speed as crack is to cocaine.

LEGAL STATUS

All the amphetamines and similar stimulants are Prescription Only drugs under the Medicines Act and are also controlled under the Misuse of Drugs Act. Doctors can still prescribe them and patients possess them if they have been prescribed, but otherwise their unauthorised production, supply or possession is an offence. It is also an offence to allow premises to be used for producing or supplying these drugs. Amphetamine and its analogues are Class B drugs, but if these are prepared for injection, the increased penalties of Class A apply.

PRODUCTION & SUPPLY

During the 1950s and 1960s when recreational use of amphetamines became widespread, they derived largely from medical sources, including excessive prescribing and pharmacy break-ins. This resulted in their control under the 1964 Dangerous Drugs Act and later a voluntary ban on prescribing by doctors. However, from the early 1970s onwards, illicitly manufactured amphetamine sulphate powder took over from illegally diverted pharmaceutical products. Nowadays, most amphetamine comes from Europe, especially Holland, but there are also underground laboratories in the UK.

PREVALENCE

Recreational use of amphetamines by teenagers (such as 'mods' taking 'purple hearts') in the early and mid-1960s died out, as the pills became less available. However, amphetamine use has never gone away. Use of amphetamine powder was common among certain youth subcultures throughout the 1970s and 1980s and, on the back of dance culture, use has increased substantially through the 1990s.

Currently, about 5% of those aged 16–29 have tried the drug in the past year, about 300,000 people. Amphetamine injectors tend to be older than other amphetamine users and have usually been using the drug for a long period of time.

The crystalline form of methamphetamine, known as Ice, has been reported at dance venues, but is still primarily a US- and Pacific Rim-based phenomenon. Use of amphetamine base is reported to be on the increase, particularly on the dance scene and among those choosing to inject, primarily due to its alleged purity and greater strength.

LICIT AND ILLICIT USE

First synthesised in 1887, the drug was not made widely available until 1932 as a decongestant nasal inhaler in the form of Benzedrine. The drug was later exploited as a stimulant to increase the performance of troops in the Second World War and the Vietnam War. High-profile users include John F. Kennedy, Adolf Hitler, who supposedly injected as well as ingested the drug, and the former Prime Minister Anthony Eden who admitted using the drug throughout the Suez crisis of 1956.

Amphetamines

In the 1950s and 1960s they were widely prescribed to treat depression and to suppress appetite, but are now recommended only (albeit controversially) for the treatment of attention deficit disorders in children, for which Ritalin is prescribed, and a pathological tendency to fall asleep (narcolepsy).

Amphetamines may be smoked, dabbed (orally consumed by dabbing small amounts each time onto the finger and into the mouth) or dissolved in soft drinks and drunk, but the illicitly manufactured powders available today are generally sniffed up the nose or injected.

In some groups the drug is used 'as required' to aid performance at manual or intellectual tasks, in others for purely recreational purposes. The drug's quality as an appetite suppressant also makes the drug popular as a slimming aid.

An occasional user might take a few weeks to consume half a gram, while a heavy user, who has developed substantial tolerance to the drug's effects, might consume anything up to several grams a day of relatively low purity substance. The smokeable form Ice is usually smoked in glass pipes similar to those used by crack users. Intravenous amphetamine use has been part of the UK drug scene since the late 1960s.

PRICE

The powder retails at an average price of £8–9 per gram. A typical £5 'wrap' of 400–500mg of powder contains 50mg of amphetamine. Amphetamine base sells for roughly £13 a gram; Ice for roughly £25 a gram, or crystal 'rock'.

SHORT-TERM USE

Amphetamines arouse and activate the user much as the body's natural adrenaline does in the face of emergencies or stress. Breathing and heart rate speed up, the pupils widen, and appetite lessens. The user feels more alert, energetic, confident and cheerful, and less bored or tired. With higher doses, intense exhilaration, rapid flow of ideas and feelings of greatly increased physical and mental capacity are common.

With some people, however, and especially as the body's energy stores become depleted, the predominant

feelings may be anxiety, irritability and restlessness. High doses, especially if frequently repeated over a few days, can produce delirium, panic, hallucinations and feelings of persecution ('amphetamine psychosis') which gradually disappear as the drug is eliminated from the body.

The effects of a single dose last about three to four hours, and leave the user feeling tired: it can take a couple of days for the body to fully recover, even after small doses.

Mixing with other drugs

The combination of one drug on top of another on mind and body can produce complex effects, as yet little understood. As a general rule, it is probable that drugs of a similar nature and action upon the body, that is two stimulants or two depressants, will have an additive effect, resulting in greater stimulation or depression, depending on the drug types. Taking, therefore, speed on top of cocaine will increase feelings of energy and activity, as well as paranoia, aggression and anxiety, not to mention a heavy drawn-out recovery period to contend with later.

Mixing drugs which bring on opposite effects, such as speed and heroin, or speed and alcohol, has more unpredictable consequences, depending on factors such as the user's mood, individual reaction to either drug, the order in which the drugs are taken, and how much of each is taken. Amphetamine taken while drunk, for example, may make one individual feel more awake and in control, or may make another feel more drunk and aggressive, exaggerating their drunken behaviour.

Combinations with hallucinogens are more complex still, with mood, current circumstances and personality playing an even greater role in drug effects. Stimulants may add to the intensity of hallucinations or visual distortions, often prolonging the experience. Depressants, on the other hand, may lessen the degree of intensity, or may enhance feelings of confusion and bring on mood swings.

There are a number of drugs, some of which are prescribed by doctors, which when taken in combination with amphetamines can cause problems. One form of anti-depressant, for example, can raise blood pressure to dangerous levels.

I am quite lazy by inclination and have had confidence problems at various stages of my life. Amphetamine seemed to solve both these problems. I didn't get tired and I didn't get self-conscious. In fact, I felt witty, energetic, powerful, amusing. For six months I thought I was God. I wrote masses, lost a lot of weight, which was bothering me at the time, and didn't have to miss out on anything through the mundane need to sleep. The use gradually escalated until I was only sleeping about three nights a week ... I woke up one day and decided I couldn't stand it any more ... There was this complete lassitude and depression in the first couple of days. I don't think I've felt quite so low in my life ... I could do virtually nothing, but what I would do was get up as early as possible, which effectively meant that after week two I was getting up at four instead of five, and a week or two after that, at noon. When I actually got to the point where eight hours' sleep was enough and I could get up at 9 am I went back to work. This took about two months, but it was 18 months before I felt I was restored to the kind of human being I'd been before taking the speed.

Writer quoted in A. Tyler, *Street Drugs*, NEL 1986

LONG-TERM USE

The mood-elevating effects of synthetic stimulants can lead to psychological dependence. After a 'run' of stimulant use or after long-term regular use, the user is likely to feel deeply depressed, lethargic and hungry, because amphetamines merely postpone fatigue and hunger – they do not satisfy the needs of the body and mind for rest and nourishment. However, abrupt cessation of stimulant use generally requires no medical assistance as physiological processes are not severely disrupted.

Tolerance develops to the stimulant effects of the amphetamines, so frequent users are tempted to increase the dose. At this stage toxic effects are liable to develop, including delusions, hallucinations and feelings of paranoia. Many experienced users are aware that their paranoia is drug-induced, but sometimes these feelings lead to hostility as stimulant users defend themselves against imagined attacks. These symptoms can persist for a time after drugtaking has stopped, but will eventually abate. In a few people they develop into a psychotic state, from which it can take several months to fully recover.

Heavy, prolonged stimulant use debilitates the user due to lack of sleep and food, and lowers resistance to disease. Users who inject the drug also run the same risks to health, as those injecting any other drug.

Amyl and butyl nitrite

Amyl, butyl and isobutyl nitrite (known collectively as alkyl nitrites) are chemically related to nitrous oxide, or laughing gas, and are inhaled. They are clear, yellow, volatile and inflammable liquids with a sweet smell when fresh, but when stale degenerate to a smell often described as 'dirty socks'.

In its medical formulation, amyl nitrite comes in small glass capsules enclosed by cotton wool. To release the drug, the top of the capsule is crushed between the fingers, giving a characteristic popping sound – hence the name 'poppers'. However, as street drugs, the alkyl nitrites (usually butyl nitrite) come in small bottles with screw or plug tops. The substance can be inhaled straight from the bottle, a cloth, or anything absorbent, such as the end of an unlit cigarette.

LEGAL STATUS

Amyl nitrite in the UK is classified as a pharmacy medicine under the Medicines Act 1968, but not butyl nitrite. This means amyl nitrite is theoretically available from any chemist without a prescription. But because amyl has been largely superseded in medical practice, few pharmacists stock it.

During 1987, the Advisory Council on the Misuse of Drugs was asked by the Home Office to consider whether alkyl nitrites should be controlled under the Misuse of Drugs Act. The Council reported to ministers that it did not consider this necessary. In 1989, police prosecution of a publican under the Offences Against the Persons Act 1861, failed. Prosecutions under the Intoxicating Substances Supply Act 1985 might be a possibility, but even if successful would only apply where the user was under 18 years old.

The Medicines and Healthcare products Regulatory Agency (MHRA), who administer medicines' legislation in the UK and have the right to make the initial determination as to whether or not a product falls within the definition of a medicinal product, believe that alkyl nitrite products can be classified as medicinal products. However, an attempt in 2001 to prosecute a manufacturer of an isobutyl nitrite product was not successful.

PRODUCTION AND SUPPLY

Butyl nitrites available for non-medical use are largely produced in the USA and marketed in the UK by wholesalers to the sex and dance industries. There is some confusion as to what are regarded as English poppers, which are thought to be only amyl nitrite, while the American types are thought to be butyl nitrite. This distinction is false as many poppers marketed as such or by British wholesalers are imported from the US. But in any event, in terms of the effects of the substances, there appears to be little to choose between any of the brands or between any of the nitrites.

They are easily available from sex shops, joke shops, at dance events, so-called 'head' shops (retailers of drug paraphernalia), or by mail order. They are sold under such trade names as 'Rush', 'Locker Room', 'Ram', 'Rock Hard', 'TNT', 'Liquid Gold', 'Thrust' and 'Hardware'.

PREVALENCE

Traditionally, poppers have been associated with the gay community. Use, however, is more widespread. It is estimated that 4% of those aged between 16 and 29 years have used the drug and use appears to be on the increase among young people aged 11–15. Between 1998–2002, the average percentage of this age group which had inhaled poppers in the previous year rose from 1–2% to 4.5%.

LICIT AND ILLICIT USE

Amyl nitrite was discovered in 1857 and put to medical use as a vasodilator in 1867 to ease the chest pains caused by angina pectoris, which it does by dilating the blood vessels and so allowing more blood to get to the heart. In recent years, amyl nitrite has been replaced by other medicines in the treatment of angina, mainly in the form of pills and inhalers. Nowadays, its main use is as an antidote to industrial cyanide poisoning. Butyl nitrite, although chemically very similar to amyl nitrite, has no recognised medical uses and has been marketed as a 'room odoriser' to avoid the legal restrictions on amyl nitrite. However, as noted above, this loophole may be closing.

Nitrites are largely bought to loosen inhibitions and produce stimulation while dancing, as well as to enhance sexual activity. The drug is used also to boost the effects of other stimulant drugs such as ecstasy.

Nitrites are regarded as a social drug in that they are passed round for use either to friends or fellow clubbers, similar to the way cigarettes or a joint may be passed round.

PRICE

Poppers usually retail in Britain from around £2–£3 per 10ml bottle, up to around £6, although prices may vary from region to region, depending on who is selling the drug and when.

SHORT-TERM USE

Once inhaled, the effects are virtually instantaneous and last for two to five minutes. There is a 'rush' as the blood vessels dilate, heartbeat quickens and the blood rushes to the brain. As a result, pounding headache, dizziness, a flushed face and neck and 'light-headedness' are commonly reported. Those using the drug to enhance sexual pleasure claim a slowed sense of time, prolonged sensation of orgasm and prevention of premature ejaculation, although some have reported problems with achieving erection. Alkyl nitrites relax the body's soft muscle tissue, such as muscles surrounding the eye and the anal sphincter.

Less common physical symptoms include nausea, headache, weakness and cold sweats. Cases of nitrite dermatitis have been reported, affecting the upper lip, nose and cheeks, sometimes accompanied by pain and swelling of the nasal passages resembling sinusitis. This clears spontaneously in about ten days and only re-occurs with resumed use. A painful burning sensation results from spilling nitrites on the skin.

Blood pressure is reduced, which could cause unconsciousness – especially if the user is lying down to inhale and then gets up quickly. Excessive use may result in a reduction of oxygen in the blood, known as methaemoglobinaemia. Symptoms can include cyanosis, when the skin and lips become blue-tinged, severe vomiting, shock and unconsciousness. An acute attack of this condition has caused fatalities, but usually in those who have swallowed rather than inhaled nitrites.

LONG-TERM USE

Tolerance develops within two or three weeks of continual use, but after a few days of abstinence, this tolerance is lost, leaving the user particularly vulnerable to headaches if use is resumed. There are no reports of withdrawal symptoms or psychological dependence – although repeated use as a sex aid and stimulant is not uncommon.

As the drug is excreted rapidly from the body, there appears to be no serious long-term consequences from the inhalation of nitrites by healthy adults.

The use of alkyl nitrites has been linked to the development of a rare cancer known as Kaposi's sarcoma, which is one of the earliest symptoms of AIDS in those gay men who are HIV positive. The link was made because most of the earliest AIDS cases were gay men who had used nitrites, substances shown to include possibly carcinogenic compounds. Even at the time, there were conflicting studies on this; nowadays there is even less support for the theory, although it may still be the case that along with many other substances, nitrites act to depress the immune system. However, the significance of this in the development of AIDS is not known and many study results are inconclusive.

SPECIAL CASES

Anyone with a history of heart trouble or other cardiovascular problems such as anaemia should avoid using nitrites. The drug's ability to relax soft muscles and dilate blood vessels, thereby producing a rapid drop in blood pressure may cause the user to pass out, possibly causing damage to the brain and other organs. Inhalation of nitrites causes increased pressure within the eye, so using them could cause problems for those with glaucoma. Pfizer, the manufacturers of Viagra, warn against mixing this drug with poppers.

Benzodiazepines

Benzodiazepines are the most commonly prescribed minor tranquillisers, known as anxiolytics (for daytime anxiety-relief) and hypnotics (to promote sleep). They include products such as Temazepam, Valium, Librium and Ativan. Because of a relative absence of undesirable side-effects (such as drowsiness and poor co-ordination) and their safety in overdose, since their introduction in the 1960s, benzodiazepines have come to replace barbiturates for use as sedatives and sleeping pills. They are manufactured as powders, formed into a variety of pills and capsules taken by mouth. The exception to this is Temazepam which comes as a gel in a capsule and has been widely injected by drug users. Doctors in the NHS have now been banned from prescribing this formulation of the drug.

LEGAL STATUS

All benzodiazepines are Prescription Only under the Medicines Act. This means they can only be supplied at a pharmacy by a pharmacist, in accordance with a doctor's prescription, and it is illegal under this Act to supply them in any other circumstances.

Benzodiazepines are also controlled under Class C of the Misuse of Drugs Act, which makes it illegal to supply them. The unauthorised possession of benzodiazepines became an offence in 2000 under an amendment of the Misuse of Drugs Act. Those possessing them without a proper prescription are liable to prosecution.

The possession of illicitly produced benzodiazepines would be an offence and people can still be prosecuted for stealing or committing fraud or some other non-drug offence to obtain the drugs.

There are also restrictions on the import and export of these drugs, requiring licences to do so, other than for patients travelling abroad for less than a month.

PRODUCTION AND SUPPLY

There is no known illicit manufacture of benzodiazepines. The benzodiazepines which circulate on the illicit market are diverted from legitimate clients either by over-prescription, that is to say individuals selling on, part or, all of their legitimately prescribed drugs, or by theft from pharmacies, hospitals or wholesalers.

PREVALENCE

Surveys suggest that about one in seven British adults take benzodiazepines at some time during the year, and 1 in 40 take them throughout the year. The proportion of women using prescribed psychotropics is double the proportion of men. From a position in 1991, where the number of prescriptions for diazepam (3.2 million) was about half that for temazepam (6.4 million) – diazepam prescriptions in 2002 (4.6 million) overtook temazepam (4.1 million).

LICIT AND ILLICIT USE

Benzodiazepines are the most commonly prescribed psychotropic drugs in Britain. About 80% of benzodiazepines are prescribed for sleeping problems, anxiety or mental distress, but in a substantial proportion of patients (as many as half in some studies) these problems are associated with physical complaints.

As a street drug, they are usually used to see the user over periods when their main drug of choice is unavailable, or to augment the effects of other depressant-type drugs, such as alcohol or opiates, or to offset the effects of stimulants such as ecstasy and amphetamine sulphate. However, injectable temazepam is also a street drug of choice. The manufacturers changed the original formulation from liquid capsule to gel to try and prevent users injecting, but the practice continues – users simply heat the drug to liquefy it for injection.

PRICE

Individual 10mg diazepam tablets sell for between 50 pence to £1. They are usually sold in batches of at least four for around £3, or £8 for 20. Twenty-milligrams temazepam tablets sell for 50 pence to £1 each; flunitrazepam (Rohypnol) tablets for £1–£1.50 each.

> I now think of this time of my life as the period when I had been chemically lobotomised.
>
> Peter Ritson, *Alive and Kicking: a True Story*, CASA, 1989

SHORT-TERM USE

Benzodiazepines depress mental activity and alertness, but are effective in doses which do not generally make people drowsy or impair clarity of thought as much as barbiturates. Nevertheless, some people do feel drowsy and lethargic and may be forgetful after first taking them, and they do impair driving and similar skills: these side-effects generally fade after a week or two of regular use. Benzodiazepines relieve tension and anxiety, and induce feelings of calmness and relaxation. This relief may be experienced as pleasure, but in non-anxious individuals benzodiazepines do not generally produce positive feelings of pleasure or well-being, accounting for their lack of popularity as recreational drugs. Probably due to its relative speed of action, diazepam (Valium) is occasionally an exception to this rule, and can produce mild euphoria, lasting three to six hours.

Any benzodiazepine in a high enough dose can induce sleep, and if long-acting varieties (like Mogadon or Dalmane) are used, the sedative effect can last into the next day.

Many more benzodiazepines than barbiturates have to be taken for a fatal overdose, but, like the other effects described, this effect is reached at a lower dosage level if alcohol has also been taken. When mixed with other drugs, in particular alcohol, the user will usually experience feelings of extreme intoxication, losing inhibitions, appearing physically very drunk.

On the streets, users have liquefied gel Temazepam for injection. Unfortunately, the gel re-solidifies in the veins and can cause serious problems; some users have lost limbs through this practice.

LONG-TERM USE

Tolerance develops to both the therapeutic and the non-therapeutic effects. After up to two-weeks' regular use, benzodiazepines may become ineffective as sleeping pills, and after four months, ineffective against anxiety. It has been estimated that at least half of those continually taking benzodiazepines for more than a year, do so due to dependence rather than because the drug is still medically effective. However, there are few studies directly relevant to the issue of dependence as opposed to withdrawal symptoms.

Dependence is mainly psychological in nature. The 'pills' are relied upon to help cope with situational pressures or psychological problems, and there may be severe anxiety and panic if the drug is temporarily unavailable. Dependence on and excessive use of benzodiazepines is particularly likely among those with a history of dependence on similar drugs, such as alcohol or barbiturates.

Sometimes severe withdrawal symptoms can occur if tolerance effects or stressful life events have led the patient to increase the dose. Generally, mild withdrawal symptoms can occur in a substantial minority of patients after a few years' treatment with normal therapeutic doses, and in the majority after six to eight years. Withdrawal effects after suddenly stopping benzodiazepines often take several days to appear and last two/three weeks or longer. They can include insomnia, anxiety, perceptual hypersensitivity, tremor, irritability, nausea and vomiting, and, after unusually high doses, may include mental confusion and even life-threatening convulsions. Withdrawal symptoms seem particularly noticeable with shorter-acting benzodiazepine, such as Lorazepam and Temazepam. Because the withdrawal syndrome can resemble the original complaint, both patient and doctor may be tempted to continue the treatment.

Cocaine and crack

Cocaine (cocaine hydrochloride) is a white powder derived from the leaves of the Andean coca shrub, Erythroxylum coca, with powerful stimulant properties similar to those of amphetamines. Coca leaf chewing may have been practised among South American Indians as long ago as 2500bc, and natives in the growing regions of South America still use the leaves as an aid to arduous or extended work. Up until 1904 Coca-Cola contained small quantities of cocaine, and a coca-laced tonic wine was enjoyed by nineteenth-century aristocracy.

Due to its expense, cocaine was seen for a long time as a 'jet set' drug, the illicit equivalent of champagne; and in some South American producer countries cocaine profits are a major corrupting influence on the economy. Recent increases in cocaine's availability have reduced its price, but the glamour associated with the drug seems undiminished.

Cocaine is injected, sometimes mixed with heroin, but more commonly a small amount is sniffed up the nose through a tube and absorbed into the blood supply via the nasal membranes.

Cocaine is also smoked through a process known as freebasing, whereby the cocaine base is 'freed' from the acid hydrochloride. 'Crack' is simply freebased cocaine produced by an easier method, resulting in small rocks of cocaine each about the size of a raisin.

LEGAL STATUS

In Britain during the First World War, unfounded rumours about cocaine use among the troops (the main legal producer for medical purposes being Germany) led to its prohibition under emergency laws. These were continued in the first Dangerous Drugs Act of 1920.

Cocaine, its various salts and the leaves of the coca plant, are now controlled in Class A of the Misuse of Drugs Act. Coca leaf is under a set of regulations that envisage no medical uses, so it can only be supplied or possessed by persons licensed by the Home Secretary for research or other special purposes. The only restriction on cocaine-prescribing for therapeutic purposes is that, as with some opiates, a doctor must be licensed by the Home Office before s/he can use the drug to treat

anything other than physical illness. This means that most doctors cannot prescribe cocaine as a way of dealing with addiction. Such use is, however, very uncommon. It is also illegal to allow premises to be used for producing or supplying cocaine.

PRODUCTION AND SUPPLY

The isolation of the alkaloid cocaine from the coca leaf was first perfected in 1860 by Albert Nieman at Göttingen University, and provided the first local anaesthetic available to modern medicine. Several thousand tons of the drug are currently produced annually (not all illicitly) by the three main cocaine-producing countries of the world – Colombia, Bolivia and Peru. Trafficking routes out of these areas vary. Countries such as Panama, Argentina and Brazil operate as the first point of call, often shipping large quantities of the drug to Florida and Europe via the West Indies and Africa.

The illicit production process typically goes through three key stages. In makeshift labs, the harvested leaf is soaked and dissolved in water, acid and other agents, such as solvents and lime. The solution is filtered, producing a semi pure paste known as base, *basa*, *pitillo* or *basuco*. Although uncommon in the UK, this dark paste is popular in areas where cocaine is produced. Users prefer to smoke the drug in cigarettes or in cannabis joints. The final process takes the paste through several stages of refinement, using such agents as benzine, alcohol and sulphuric acid. The resulting crystalline residue typically contains 90% cocaine hydrochloride. On its way to the streets in the UK and elsewhere, the cocaine is repeatedly mixed or cut with other agents, usually glucose powder, until it is sold at around 20–50% purity.

Crack is in essence a reversal of the last stage of production, involving the baking of cocaine in water and soda or ammonia to produce large crystals of cocaine, 'freed' from its hydrochloride base in a smokeable form. Crack is usually processed closer to the illicit market, often by drug dealers in their own kitchens.

Since the expansion of the cocaine market in the USA in the 1980s, cocaine production and supply have been controlled by a number of powerful cartels. The wealth and power of these cartels, many based in Colombia, have attracted a great deal of international interest,

> Everyone who tries crack will not like the high and everyone who likes the high will not become instantly and hopelessly addicted.
>
> M.G. Beattie, *Crack: the Facts*, Hazelden Foundation, 1987

particularly from the USA. Large budgets are spent annually by the USA on aiding the governments of the producer countries trying to control the production and trafficking of the drug, by crop spraying, the movement of troops and intelligence staff, or by the seizure of 'precursor chemicals' (basic chemicals used in the production process).

The case of Pablo Escobar, one of the world's most notorious and wealthy cocaine barons until his assassination by CIA- and FBI-backed police officers in 1993, is a typical example of how seriously western governments take the influence of the powerful cartels. At his height, Escobar was estimated to be worth $5 billion and responsible for four-fifths of the world's trade in cocaine. The US government's pursuit of Escobar spanned over ten years of intelligence work, involving the governments and troops of four nations and the use of large bounties for the heads of prominent gang leaders. These efforts resulted in the death of Escobar, only to bring a shift of power and control of much of the world's cocaine market to a wider array of smaller cartels.

PREVALENCE

In general, the expense of cocaine can still be expected to limit its regular use to a small percentage of the population, but that percentage seems to be on the increase as prices have fallen. Cocaine has been used by 3% of the adult population and by 12% of those aged 20 to 24 years old.

LICIT AND ILLICIT USE

Since its introduction in the early 1860s, cocaine has been put to a number of uses, legitimate or otherwise. From 1860 onwards, the drug was made widely available as a decongestant and a remedy for asthma. The drug was most popular as an additive to drinks, such as Vin Mariani wine and Coca-Cola, marketed as

a 'brain tonic'. Enthusiastic proponents included the Grand Rabbi of France, Pope Pius X, Queen Victoria, and Leo XIII, who awarded Mariani a gold medal. Freud championed the use of cocaine in 1884, advocating it for ailments such as hysteria, depression, syphilis and even morphine addiction. Later put to use as a local anaesthetic, it was gradually replaced by alternative drugs and is today only rarely used for topical anaesthesia of the upper respiratory tract, that is to say the throat. Concerns about the sale of medicines containing cocaine, and the risk of addiction, led to its eventual control in the USA in 1914. In the UK, worries about British troops being under the influence of German-produced cocaine led to its ban under the Defence of the Realm Act in 1916 and control under the Dangerous Drugs Act of 1920.

However, probably because of the ready availability of legal amphetamines and the reduction in medical supplies of the drug, cocaine was not much in evidence on the illicit drug scene until it reappeared among American film and rock stars of the late 1960s.

In the mid-1970s cocaine sniffing gained popularity. This was originally located in the world of entertainment, especially the music and film industries, and then in the 1980s became anecdotally a 'fashion accessory' for the younger members of the City of London's Square Mile. It also came to be used on an occasional basis by a broader section of the drug using population: recent surveys indicate an increasing use of cocaine in the UK.

A smokeable variety, known as crack, has now become common in areas of traditional chronic problematic drug use, mainly (but not exclusively) inner city areas suffering acute social deprivation – and may also be

> The first hit is always the best ... I've never had anything like it. With crack once you've got that first hit of the day, no matter how much you take you don't get it back. If the rock is there, I can't leave it, even though I don't get anything off it. But you can't just have one (rock) and leave it, you've got to have more.
>
> Quoted in *Crack and Cocaine in England and Wales*, Home Office, 1992

Cocaine and crack

found on the dance scene and among more general drug using circles.

The typical 'weekend' user might sniff one-quarter gram or so over the weekend; regular users with sufficient resources might consume one to two grams a day. Because the effects wear off very quickly, users can get through several grams (and thus hundreds of pounds) at a stretch.

PRICE

Although more expensive than amphetamine, people already involved in drugtaking circles can currently obtain cocaine at around £40 – £80 per gram, averaged out for the whole of the United Kingdom. The purer the cocaine the higher the price, but prices above £100 are uncommon. Prices seem to be lower in the South-East where £50 to £60 can typically buy the user a gram of 40 to 50% pure cocaine. Crack is available in many parts of the country, retailing at around £25 weighing 150mgs and about 88% pure, although samples of 100% purity are not unknown. Smaller slivers of crack may be sliced from a 'rock' and sold more cheaply.

SHORT-TERM USE

Like amphetamine, cocaine produces physiological arousal accompanied by exhilaration, feelings of well-being, decreased hunger, indifference to pain and fatigue, and feelings of great physical strength and mental capacity. Sometimes these desired effects are replaced by anxiety or panic. When sniffed, the psychological effects peak after about 15–30 minutes and then diminish, meaning the dose may have to be repeated every 20 minutes to maintain the effect. When smoked as crack the effects are almost immediate and very intense, but more short-lived.

Large doses or a 'spree' of quickly repeated doses over a period of hours can lead to an extreme state of agitation, anxiety, paranoia, and perhaps hallucination. As with amphetamine psychosis, these effects generally resolve themselves as the drug is eliminated from the body. The after-effects of cocaine use include fatigue and depression, but are less noticeable than the corresponding effects after amphetamine use. These effects are said to be stronger for crack use. Excessive doses can cause death from respiratory or heart failure.

> I imagined everybody was looking at me and watching me; even when locked in my room. I could not persuade myself there were not watchers outside, with eyes glued to imaginary peepholes ... I realized the folly of thinking that spies were in the rooms above, watching me through holes pierced in the ceiling. Yet the overpowering desire to repeat the dose would overtake me...
>
> Quoted in J.L. Phillips and R.D. Wynne, *Cocaine: the Mystique and the Reality*, Avon, 1980

As with heroin, cocaine is likely to be adulterated with substances which may be harmful when injected.

Mixing with other drugs

Cocaine is typically taken at the same time as other substances such as alcohol, tobacco or cannabis (some regular users may also combine the drug with amphetamine, ecstasy and even heroin). The most likely combination is alcohol and cocaine and it is not uncommon for users rushing on cocaine to increase their subsequent intake of alcohol. Research in the USA has also suggested that when these two substances are combined, a third substance, cocaethylene, is produced. While it is too early to understand the effects of this combination on behaviour, it is suggested that the combined effect on the heart, which raises blood pressure and therefore sensitivity to the drugs, and the increased length of time cocaethylene stays in the body (three times as long as cocaine alone), will thus prolong psychosomatic effects, and so increase the likelihood that users will tend to seek these drugs in combination rather than on their own.

There is evidence linking cocaine with deaths in police custody of people in states of 'excited delirium', who die unexpectedly under certain forms of physical restraint.

Cocaine combined with other drugs can have unpredictable and often disturbing effects, particularly if the drug's effects are antagonistic. Cocaine taken with, for example heroin, known as a speedball, can enhance the effects of one or other of the drugs, to the extent that quantities of heroin familiar to the user may be sufficient to cause overdose.

Cocaine is particularly dangerous if taken with some hypertensive drugs and certain anti-depressants. When taken along with monoamine oxidase inhibitors (MAOIs), for example, cocaine (and other stimulants) is known to interfere with the body's breakdown of fatty acids or amines, caused by the MAOI inhibition. These acids, found in mature cheeses, wine, beer, bananas, some pears, and drinks like coffee, if allowed to build in the body can raise blood pressure to dangerous levels.

LONG-TERM USE

Neither tolerance nor heroin-like withdrawal symptoms occur with repeated use of cocaine, but users may well develop a strong psychological dependence on the grandiose feelings of physical and mental well-being afforded by the drug, and are often tempted to step up the dose. After discontinuing, the user will feel fatigued, sleepy and depressed (though not as severely as following repeated amphetamine use), all of which reinforce the temptation to repeat the dose. Dependence appears more likely and more severe and its onset more rapid if cocaine is smoked.

With chronic frequent use, increasingly unpleasant symptoms develop which generally persuade people to 'give it a break'. Euphoria is replaced by an uncomfortable state of restlessness, hyperexcitability, nausea, insomnia and weight loss. With continued use this may develop into a state of mind similar to paranoid psychosis. Regular users who do not use sufficiently to become manifestly psychotic may nevertheless appear chronically nervous, excitable and paranoid, and confused exhaustion due to lack of sleep is not unusual. All these effects generally clear up once use is discontinued.

Repeated sniffing damages the membranes lining the nose and may also damage the structure separating the nostrils. Repeated smoking may cause respiratory problems such as cracked, wheezy breathing and also partial loss of voice. Long-term injection produces abscesses and injecting generally exposes the user to the special risks of this method of administration.

Opiates

Opiates are a group of drugs derived from the opium poppy, with generally similar effects, notably analgesia. Opiates and their synthetic equivalents are sometimes collectively known as 'opioids', although strictly speaking, the term 'opioids' only applies to the synthetic drugs of this type. As well as being prescribed as painkillers, opiates have medical uses as cough suppressants and anti-diarrhoea agents.

The relative speed of action of heroin and the relative absence of undesirable side-effects associated with other opiates (e.g. nausea, vomiting, constipation) have made it the opiate preferred by many drug users, while its potency relative to other opiates makes smuggling of smaller amounts more profitable. As with other drugs, intravenous injection maximises the effects.

LEGAL STATUS

In the nineteenth century opiates were a popular panacea, available without prescription from grocers and other shops in the UK. Professional self-interest, awareness of the dangers of poisoning and dependence, fears that the working class might be unprofitably diverted – all these forces combined to prompt the first restrictions of 1868. After the First World War, Britain implemented an international agreement and prohibited non-medical use of opium and opiates. Nevertheless, Britain has never denied that opiates – including heroin – could be prescribed to those who couldn't cope without the drug.

In the 1960s, younger users emerged, who 'recycled' surplus heroin obtained from a few GPs. As a result addiction spread, and in 1968 all but a few specialists were prohibited from prescribing heroin for addiction and special treatment clinics were established. Not necessarily as a result, the mid-1970s saw the beginnings of a significant black market in imported, illicitly manufactured heroin.

Opiates are controlled under the Misuse of Drugs Act, making it illegal to supply or to possess them without a prescription, and penalising unauthorised production, import or export. It is also an offence to allow premises to be used for producing or supplying these drugs.

The long history of opium legislation has left anachronistic provisions, making it an offence to use opium (the only prohibition on actual drug use in the Act); to frequent a place used for opium smoking; or even to possess utensils for smoking or preparing opium. It is also an offence to allow premises to be used for preparing or smoking opium.

Only specially licensed doctors can prescribe heroin, dipipanone and cocaine for anything other than physical illness. This means most doctors cannot prescribe these drugs as a way of dealing with dependence. Apart from this, all opiates can be prescribed for their normal therapeutic uses.

Heroin, morphine, opium, methadone, dipipanone (Diconal) and pethidine appear in Class A of the Act. Codeine is Class B (unless prepared for injection when it becomes Class A). Dextropropoxyphene (Distalgesic and other preparations) and buprenorphine (Temgesic) are in Class C.

Some very dilute mixtures of codeine, morphine or opium (used as cough medicines or to treat diarrhoea) are exempt from most of the restrictions and can be bought over the counter from pharmacies.

PRODUCTION AND SUPPLY

Opium is the dried 'milk' of the opium poppy. It contains morphine and codeine, both effective painkillers. From morphine it is not difficult to produce heroin, which in pure form is a fluffy white powder over twice as potent as morphine. Heroin is a synthetically modified opium alkaloid, known as diamorphine in its purest medical form, first synthesised in 1898 by the German pharmaceutical company Bayer. Street heroin is a poor cousin of medical heroin, usually brown instead of the pure white, indicating its crude beginning as opium paste. A number of 'synthetic opiates' are manufactured as painkillers. These include pethidine, often used in childbirth; dipipanone (Diconal); and methadone (Physeptone), the drug usually prescribed for opiate dependence.

Most of today's medical heroin originates from India and Afghanistan (some from other countries such as Tasmania) where large quantities of legitimate poppy fields produce opium sufficient for over five million of opiate-based prescriptions in England every year. Although licensed doctors can still prescribe heroin to

> It's not only a question of kicks. The ritual itself, the powder in the spoon, the little ball of cotton, the matches applied, the bubbling liquid drawn up through the cotton filter into the eye-dropper; the tie around the arm to make a vein stand out ... all this is not for nothing; it is born of a respect for the whole chemistry of alienation.
>
> Alexander Trocchi, *Cain's Book*, Quartet, 1973

addicts, most choose not to, so very little prescribed heroin reaches the illicit market. The vast majority of illicit heroin is grown and produced in small- to medium-scale farms and makeshift laboratories in two areas, known as the Golden Crescent (mainly Afghanistan and Pakistan) which supplies about 75% of the world market for heroin and the Golden Triangle (Burma, Laos and Thailand) which supplies most of the rest.

Converted into heroin either on site or en route, the heroin makes its way along a number of well-known trade routes, such as Turkey and the Balkans. However new sources and routes are continually emerging, with ex-Soviet bloc countries now being identified as key controllers and traffickers of heroin from countries such as China and Afghanistan. The Netherlands imports and then exports much of the heroin into the UK, mainly to London and the South-East.

Countries such as Colombia and Peru, known for their production of cocaine, are also (along with Mexico) increasing the production of heroin. This is causing an upturn in the amount of heroin available in the US and also having an impact on supplies into continental Europe and the UK.

Starting from upwards of 95% purity in the country of origin, street heroin is typically mixed, or cut, with various adulterants to anything from 20 to 50% purity. Unusually high purity heroin or heroin cut with toxins or agents, which clog the blood, have led to some heroin-related deaths, as did a batch of heroin lethally contaminated with bacteria of unknown origin.

PREVALENCE

Since the late 1970s, opiate availability, use and dependence have all substantially increased, largely due to the increased availability of illicitly imported heroin.

The lowest current estimate in the updated drug strategy is 250,000, but recent Home Office research conducted by York University indicated use levels in the range of 280,000–500,000.

LICIT AND ILLICIT USE

Opiate powders can be swallowed or dissolved in water and injected. Heroin is rarely swallowed (as this is relatively ineffective) but can be sniffed like cocaine or smoked. When smoked, heroin powder is heated on tin foil and the fumes inhaled, commonly through a small tube, a practice known as 'chasing the dragon'. Opium itself is either eaten or smoked. Some opiate mixtures are effectively rendered non-injectable by the substances used to dissolve the powder, one reason why methadone mixture is frequently prescribed to opiate addicts. Chronic users generally inject, but recreational use of heroin has developed among people in their late teens, with the drug being sniffed, smoked and injected. In an era of greater awareness about the dangers of injecting, statistics indicate that the numbers of those injecting heroin are falling slightly.

Besides those dependent on heroin, some people are dependent on synthetic opiates obtained by theft from pharmacies or from doctors. In times of difficulty it is not unusual for opiate users to resort to tranquillisers or sedatives, or to drinking large quantities of opiate-based cough medicines available without prescription from pharmacies; some people restrict their opiate misuse to these preparations.

PRICE

Since 1995, prices have fallen significantly from around £80 a gram to less than £40 in some regions. Smaller

> Boils and abscesses plague the skin; gnawing pain racks the body. Nerves snap; vicious twitching develops. Imaginary and fantastic fears blight the mind and sometimes complete insanity results. Often times, too, death comes – much too early in life ... Such is the torment of being a drug addict; such is the plague of being one of the walking dead.
>
> U.S. Supreme Court, 1962

Opiates

quantities such as one-quarter gram bags retail at around £20 to £25. An addict might use one-quarter to half gram each day.

Heroin will be diluted (or adulterated) with a variety of powders of similar appearance, such as glucose powder, chalk dust, caffeine, quinine, flour and talcum powder, and other drug substances like phenobarbitone powder. However, evidence from the Forensic Science Service shows that purity levels are not that much different between heroin seized on entry into the UK and that seized on the street. Average purity is 40–45%.

Methadone retails for a near universal price of £1 per 10ml. A user will typically buy in quantities of 50ml to 100ml, or in ampoules of 25ml at £25 per unit.

SHORT-TERM USE

Pure opiates in moderate doses produce a range of generally mild physical effects, apart from analgesia, and a number of these have medical applications. Like sedatives they depress nervous system activity, including reflex functions such as coughing, respiration and heart rate. They also dilate blood vessels (giving a feeling of warmth) and depress bowel activity, resulting in constipation.

Even at levels sufficient to produce euphoria, there is little interference with sensation, motor skills or intellect. At higher doses, sedation takes over and the user becomes drowsy and contented. Excessive doses produce stupor and coma. Death from respiratory failure is possible, but unlikely unless there are contributory factors, such as other depressant drugs used at the same time, loss of tolerance or unexpected potency.

There can also be fatal reactions to injected adulterants. With the uncertain composition and purity of street heroin, adverse reactions are an ever-present possibility. With more people coming forward for treatment, there are increasing numbers of people who are overdosing on prescribed methadone.

There is much confusion about the initial heroin experience. A large proportion of people report drowsiness, warmth, well-being and contentment. Pleasurable feelings are associated with the fact that opiates induce relaxed detachment from the impact of pain and anxiety, and from desires for food and sex, even at the same time as the person remains fully aware.

Along with or instead of these reactions, first use (especially injection) is often accompanied by nausea and vomiting. Whether this deters people will depend on their motivations for continuing and the strength of the euphoria. These unpleasant reactions quickly disappear with repeated doses.

Injection into the veins intensifies these effects and makes them almost instantaneous, producing a short-lived burst of pleasurable sensation ('rush'). Injection under the skin or into the muscle gives a slower and less intense effect. Sniffing heroin also gives a slower and less intense effect than intravenous injection. When smoked, the effects of heroin can be expected to come on about as quickly as intravenous injection, but to be much less intense as the available dose is used over a period of time rather than injected all at once.

Mixing with other drugs

Heroin users are often users of other drugs, either separately or in combination with their heroin. There are a few traditional drug mixes, such as the speedball, a heroin and cocaine cocktail, which gives the user a combination of stimulation and the depressant effects discussed above – a pleasurable experience to some but not without its dangers to the heart and kidneys and the general risk of overdose.

> *Interviewer:* Why did you try heroin again, if you got sick from it the first time?
> *Addict 1:* 'Cause I liked, you know, like the high.
> *Interviewer:* You said you got sick?
> *Addict 1:* I got sick, but I got loaded. Got bombed ... You get sick at the stomach, you know, but when you're loaded, you just don't care. [You] just sit there nodding. [If you] feel sick, you just go, come back, and you nod some more.
> *Addict 2:* Well, I know one broad in particular. She begged me to give her ... a shot, and she got deathly sick. And that was the last time she used it.*Interviewer:* Did she say anything about it?
> *Addict 2:* She said, if that's the way it is, she didn't want anything to do with it.
>
> W.E. McAuliffe. 'A Second Look at First Effects: the Subjective Effects of Opiates', *Journal of Drug Issues*, 5(4) 369–399, 1975

When heroin is hard to get or is expensive, users sometimes complement their heroin with other depressants such as benzodiazepines, including Valium and Temazepam, as well as, barbiturates and often alcohol. Combinations can be difficult to control, and in high enough doses can lead to overdose.

LONG-TERM USE

Tolerance develops to opiates so that someone in search of frequently repeated euphoria must increase the dose and/or change their method of administration. However, there comes a point when no further increases in dose can restore the positive effects of the drug and it is taken just to feel 'normal'. Intravenous injection maximises the effects of a given amount of heroin and produces a much more intense, immediate experience, so as tolerance develops (and perhaps as money runs short) there may be a tendency to move from sniffing or smoking heroin to injection. Since (unlike the barbiturates) tolerance also develops to the respiratory depressant effects of opiates, gradual escalation of dose does not in itself lead to risk of death through overdose. However, fatal overdoses can happen when opiate users take their usual dose after a break during which tolerance has faded.

After as little as several weeks on high, frequent doses, sudden withdrawal results in a variable degree of discomfort, generally comparable to a bout of influenza. The effects start 8 to 24 hours after the last 'fix' and include aches, tremor, sweating and chills, sneezing and yawning, and muscular spasms. They generally fade in seven to ten days, but feelings of weakness and loss of well-being last for several months. Abrupt opiate withdrawal is rarely life-threatening and is considerably less dangerous than withdrawal from alcohol.

Physical dependence is not as significant as the strong psychological dependence developed by some long-term users. Dependence of any kind is not inevitable and some people use heroin on an occasional basis.

The physiological effects of long-term opiate use are rarely serious in themselves. They include respiratory complaints, constipation and menstrual irregularity. At higher doses chronic sedation can occur, but at moderate doses users can function normally. However, the consequences of injecting opiates and of a drug-using lifestyle can be serious. Among regular injectors, there is commonly physical damage associated with poor hygiene and the injection of adulterants. Adulterants contribute to respiratory disease, skin lesions, tetanus (with injection under the skin) and other complications, depending on the agent used and the individual's sensitivity. Decreased appetite and apathy can contribute to disease caused by poor nutrition, self-neglect and bad housing. Repeated heroin sniffing may damage structures in the nose.

On the other hand, because opiates in themselves are relatively safe drugs, addicts in receipt of opiates on prescription and who maintain a stable, hygienic lifestyle, can be virtually indistinguishable from non-drug users, and suffer no serious physical damage. However, as opiates are the most commonly injected drugs of misuse in Britain, those users who do inject face a high risk of becoming infected with blood-borne viruses such as HIV and Hepatitis B and C.

Opiate use during pregnancy may result in smaller babies, who may suffer severe withdrawal symptoms after birth.

Cannabis

Cannabis is derived from the cannabis plant, a bushy plant found wild in most parts of the world and easily cultivated in Britain. There are three varieties of the plant, Cannabis sativa, indica and ruderalis. In Western countries it is generally used as a relaxant and mild intoxicant.

The most important psychoactive ingredients are the tetrahydro-cannabinols (THC). They are concentrated in resin exuded mainly at the tops of the plant. 'Hashish' or 'hash', the commonest form of cannabis in the UK, is resin scraped or rubbed from the plant, and then compressed into brown blocks. Herbal cannabis, known in the USA as marihuana, is a less strong preparation of the dried plant material. Less common in the UK is cannabis oil, generally prepared by percolating a solvent through the resin. Nowadays, cannabis with very high THC content ('skunk', 'northern lights', 'white widow') is regularly grown in the UK using seeds/plants imported mainly from the Netherlands.

LEGAL STATUS

In Britain, the non-medical use of cannabis was prohibited in 1928, after a denunciation by the Egyptian delegate persuaded an international opium conference to include it in an agreement adopted by the UK. Cannabis in its various forms is now controlled by the Misuse of Drugs Act, under regulations that prohibit its medical as well as its non-medical use. This means it is illegal to cultivate, produce, supply or possess the drug, except in accordance with a Home Office licence issued for research or other special purposes. It is an offence to allow premises to be used for producing (including cultivating), supplying of or smoking cannabis. This last type of offence – allowing the use of a drug – applies only to permitting the smoking of cannabis or opium. Since January 2004, herbal cannabis (everything except seeds and stalks) and cannabis resin are in Class C of the Act.

In 1995 the MDA was amended, placing dronabinol (a THC derivative), into Schedule 2, allowing doctors to prescribe the drug to named cancer patients for use as an anti-emetic. One pharmaceutical company now has a Home Office licence to grow low-THC content cannabis, with a view to producing medicinal cannabis-based products, and another company has taken out a patent on cannabis 'aerosols'.

PRODUCTION AND SUPPLY

As hemp, cannabis has a long history as a commercial product for the making of clothes, lighting oil, paper and rope. Cultivation can be traced as far back as the fourth millennium bc in China. Nowadays, there is a sizeable industry promoting the use of hemp as a fibre for fashion garments and health products. In an interesting synergy, the cigarette paper industry is also using hemp-based paper in its manufacturing process.

In the UK, illicit cannabis originates from a number of sources, some from home-grown UK crops, most from foreign crops brought through a number of trade routes – some new, some well trodden. North Africa, in particular Morocco, is Europe's main supplier, with Spain and Gibraltar through France a favoured transit route. Afghanistan and Pakistan are also important producers of cannabis. Routes traditionally make their way through the Balkans and Germany to the UK, with the ex-Soviet Union currently proving to be a major player in the trafficking of cannabis into the UK.

Home Office figures show that production from within Europe is steadily on the increase. With the introduction of hardy hybrids and the increasing availability of specialist growing equipment, seizures of cannabis crops, many destined for the UK, are on the increase in the Netherlands and Belgium.

The UK is also experiencing an expansion in the home-grown trade, mainly for personal use or distribution among friends.

PREVALENCE

Cannabis has the greatest non-medical usage of the drugs controlled under the Misuse of Drugs Act. Overall, about 15 million people in the UK would admit to having tried it, with around two to five million regular users. The most recent British Crime Survey revealed that a quarter of the adult population have tried the drug and half of 16- to 24-year-olds have taken it at least once. Half of this group are thought to be using, if not regularly, at least occasionally. This data supports the impression that cannabis smoking is now established in the leisure activity of a significant cross-section of the

> Music is beautiful when you're high. Every note is separate, perfect and complete – similarly every word. Beauty and love is epitomized in each note. Your hearing becomes so acute – you can hear sounds miles away and differentiation between different tones, notes, sounds, no matter how close in tone they might be to one another, is heard without any effort or thought. Your eyesight is affected also. Things become more defined, distinct, more silhouetted – colours are more beautiful. There's nothing I enjoy more when I'm smashed than to sit in a garden full of flowers, with birds singing, while the sun is going down. I really saw God in his own wonder then, for the first time.
>
> J. Berke and C. Hernton, *The Cannabis Experience*, Peter Owen, 1974

population, with even the more elderly accessing the drug for medicinal purposes, as recent high-profile court cases have shown.

LICIT AND ILLICIT USE

Cannabis was first documented as a herbal remedy in a Chinese pharmacy text of the first century AD and continued to be available on prescription in the UK – but latterly not much used – until 1973. There is growing evidence that cannabis may be effective in providing symptomatic relief for diseases of the muscular-skeletal system like Multiple Sclerosis, as an anti-nausea drug in chemotherapy, and to relieve intra-ocular pressure in glaucoma patients.

Recreational use of cannabis also dates back to ancient China and later became established in India. In the 1960s cannabis smoking emerged from immigrant groups and from the 1950s jazz clubs, to involve significant proportions of the youthful population.

In the UK, cannabis is generally smoked with tobacco in a joint or spliff, but can also be smoked in a pipe, brewed into a drink or cooked into food. Regular users might consume one-eighth of an ounce per week; heavy and regular cannabis users might use that amount in a day. Roughly one-sixteenth ounce of cannabis resin would be sufficient to produce four strong or eight less potent joints. Joints are typically smoked with friends at any one time, although many also enjoy using the drug alone to enhance their perception of music or simply to relax.

It is often suggested the taking of one drug, particularly cannabis, may lead to the use of other drugs. While it is true that most people who use heroin will have previously used cannabis, they are also likely to have smoked tobacco and consumed alcohol. Only a small proportion of those who try cannabis go on to use

heroin. Importantly, though, cannabis use involves people in the buying of illegal drugs, making it more likely that they will meet with an offer of heroin, an offer which some will accept. In this example, it would be the illegality of cannabis use rather than cannabis use itself that leads most directly to contact with heroin. The Dutch Ministry of Justice, for example, has suggested that a process of escalation does exist, but only where a single criminalised market is in place. The escalation or gateway theory often features in the debate on whether cannabis should remain illegal or not. With the threat that its use may lead to the use of other drugs, many take the stance that it should remain illegal.

The cannabis debate

Perhaps because of its widespread use, the rights and wrongs of cannabis use and of prohibiting such use have continued to be the subject of much heated debate. In general, government-commissioned reports in the English-speaking world have recommended relaxation of existing cannabis laws and these views are also held by a number of academics, politicians and senior law enforcement officers. As various polls demonstrate, UK public opinion, too, is now more favourable to a more tolerant approach to cannabis and in the light of this debate, a number of high-profile organisations are examining the position of cannabis.

In 1998, the House of Lords decided to launch its own investigation into the medical evidence about cannabis, and the Royal College of Psychiatrists and the Royal College of Physicians produced a report that asserts the risk to health of cannabis and the potential of dependence, but highlights the need for a public debate and a willingness to amend existing legislation to suit the present climate.

Cannabis

The independent inquiry by the Police Federation, known as the Runciman Report (2000), found much support from politicians and the press in asking for a distinction to be made between 'soft' drugs such as cannabis, and 'hard' drugs such as heroin and cocaine, with their greater risks to health. The report proposed the MDA be changed so that it is more lenient towards cannabis possession while focusing its sanctions on heroin and cocaine – and so re-directing state funds to regulating harder drugs.

In 2002, the government announced that it was going to reclassify cannabis so that it became a Class C drug, move that mirrored developments in other European countries (e.g. Spain, Italy and Portugal) which have relaxed controls on drug use for personal consumption.

There are also questions as to the legitimacy of prosecuting users for possession under the newly applied European Court of Human Rights, which protects the right to private life.

PRICE

Prices have been falling steadily since the mid-1990s. The most commonly available type is Moroccan/soap bar resin which has about 50% market share, retailing for about £12 for one-eighth of an ounce and £60 an ounce. 'Skunk' which has about 35% market share, retails for about £20 for one-eighth of an ounce and £120 for an ounce.

Eaten, £1.50 worth of resin would be sufficient to produce the desired effects. Smoked, about the same or slightly less could be used to make a couple of cannabis cigarettes ('joints'), sufficient for a group of two or three to get mildly intoxicated.

SHORT-TERM USE

Effects depend largely on the expectations, motivations and mood of the user, on the amount used, and on the situation in which it is used. Most people do not experience very much at first, and have to learn which effects to look out for.

The most common, and also the most sought-after effects are a pleasurable state of relaxation, talkativeness, bouts of hilarity and greater appreciation of sensory experiences, including sound and colour and taste. While intoxicated, someone smoking cannabis will do less well on tasks requiring short-term memory (like forgetting what you just said), concentration, or intellectual or manual dexterity – including driving – though to some extent these effects can be reduced by effort of will. Feelings of hunger are common and, especially among inexperienced users, there may be some anxiety.

With higher doses, there may be perceptual distortion (including a feeling that much more time has elapsed than really has), forgetfulness and confusion of thought processes. Temporary and, in a small percentage of cases, severe psychological distress and confusion can occur, most often among inexperienced users, after unusually high doses, or if the user is feeling anxious or depressed. Very heavy use among those with latent or existing mental disorders may aggravate their condition. There is virtually no danger of fatal overdose.

The effects gradually start a few minutes after smoking and may last up to one hour with low doses, and for several hours with high doses. When the effect wears off, the user may feel tired. When eaten or drunk, cannabis takes longer to have an effect and the effect also lasts longer. With this method, dosage cannot be regulated as it can if the drug is smoked, so unpleasant reactions are more difficult to avoid.

I once had what is known as 'the horrors' when I had not been smoking long. The marijuana was a very strong variety, far stronger than anything I had ever smoked before, and I was in an extremely tense and unhappy personal situation. I lost all sense of time and place and had slight hallucinations – the walls came and went, objects and sounds were unreal and people looked like monsters. It was hard to breathe and I thought I was going to die and that no one would care. This feeling receded every now and then and I glimpsed reality. It lasted about half an hour and then I feel asleep.

J. Berke and C. Hernton, *The Cannabis Experience*, Peter Owen, 1974

> The regulation of the non-medical use of cannabis has been the subject of many official enquiries. These enquiries have reached strikingly uniform conclusions on the effects of cannabis use, both on the user and the community as a whole. The failure of legislators... to accept these conclusions suggests that legislative responses are affected more by the perceived social status of the users and the values and perhaps prejudices of powerful group in the community, than by careful evaluation of the pharmacological, medical and sociological evidence.
>
> South Australia Royal Commission into the Non-Medical Use of Drugs, 1978

Mixing with other drugs

Cannabis is regularly taken to enhance or detract from the effects of other drugs. Many users of ecstasy, for example, use cannabis to relax, particularly after long dance sessions, and to cushion the come down from the drug. Conversely, the drug may be used in conjunction with alcohol to increase the depressant and loosening effects both substances elicit. Combinations with other drugs may produce unexpected effects, depending on dose, mood and what else has been taken. Stronger varieties, such as skunk, may intensify the effects of other drugs such as hallucinogens or stimulants, increasing the likelihood of paranoia or anxiety.

LONG-TERM USE

There is still no conclusive evidence that long-term cannabis use causes lasting damage to physical or mental health. Experiments suggest that it may be damaging in a number of respects, but studies of cannabis users have failed to confirm these possibilities.

In particular, it is probable that (as with tobacco smoke) frequent inhalation of cannabis smoke over a period of years helps cause bronchitis and other respiratory disorders. The long-term smoking of cannabis has been recently linked with cancers in those under 40 years old, although the reports have been challenged.

Cannabis does not produce physical dependence, though mild withdrawal symptoms have been produced in experiments. Regular users can come to feel a psychological need for the drug or may rely on it as a 'social lubricant'.

A heavy user chronically intoxicated on cannabis may appear apathetic, lack energy and perform poorly at their work or education. However, such a condition seems rare and no different from what might be expected of someone chronically intoxicated on alcohol or other sedative-type drugs. There is no evidence of a special cannabis 'amotivational syndrome'.

The effects of cannabis may cause special risks for people with existing or underlying mental illness, or with lung, respiratory or heart disorders. Prolonged heavy use occasionally causes a temporary psychiatric disorder, including mental confusion and delusions.

Cannabis has been shown to affect fertility. Cannabis receptors exist in sperm and egg ducts. Regular use has been shown to slow down sperm and inhibit fertilisation. There is also the suggestion that heavy cannabis use may adversely affect the production of sperm itself.

Regular, frequent cannabis use during pregnancy may help cause premature birth with its attendant complications. However, results are conflicting, and cannabis use is likely to be just one of a number of factors affecting foetal development. Very heavy (e.g. daily) cannabis users may give birth to babies who temporarily suffer tremor and distress, and are easily startled. There is no evidence that any adverse effects persist beyond the first year of life.

LSD

D-lysergic acid diethylamide – LSD – is a white powder hallucinogenic, but the minute amounts sufficient for a 'trip' are generally mixed with other substances and formed into tablets or capsules to be taken by mouth. In solution, the drug may also be taken absorbed on paper, gelatine sheets, or in sugar cubes. The strength of these preparations is uncertain and often substances offered as LSD will turn out to contain no LSD at all.

LEGAL STATUS

The emergence of LSD as a recreational drug in the late 1950s and 1960s, plus the public reaction to it, led the UK to place LSD under misuse of drugs legislation in 1966. However, some psychotherapists continued using the drug with their patients until 1973 when the Misuse of Drugs Act came into force and LSD could only be obtained under special licence. This means it can only be supplied or possessed for research or other special purposes by persons licensed by the Home Office. Other than in these limited instances, production, supply and possession of LSD and other hallucinogens are offences under the Act. It is also an offence to allow premises to be used for the production or supply of these drugs.

In the case of the hallucinogens psilocin and psilocybin, produced naturally in plants, the legal position is more complicated. [See **Hallucinogenic mushrooms**]

PRODUCTION AND SUPPLY

LSD is derived from ergot, a fungus found growing wild on rye and other grasses. It was first produced in 1938 and its discoverer underwent the first LSD trip in 1943. It is produced in underground labs both in the UK and abroad. Countries such as Belgium and the Netherlands have been sourced as large producers. Because the drug is often soaked into blotting paper, it is easy to distribute, locally or internationally.

PREVALENCE

After a revival in use as part of the 'rave' phenomenon, all the indicators for LSD use are in decline. According to the British Crime Survey, those aged 16–29 reporting use of LSD in the previous year fell from 3.9% in 1994 to 1.9% in 2000.

> Last Friday, April 16, 1943, I was forced to interrupt my work in the laboratory in the middle of the afternoon and proceed home, being affected by a remarkable restlessness, combined with a slight dizziness. At home I lay down and sank into a not unpleasant intoxicated-like condition, characterised by an extremely stimulated imagination. In a dreamlike state, with eyes closed, I perceived an uninterrupted stream of fantastic pictures, extraordinary shapes with intense, kaleidoscopic play of colours. After some two hours this condition faded away.
>
> Albert Hofmann, *LSD: My Problem Child*, McGraw-Hill, 1980

LICIT AND ILLICIT USE

In the 1950s and 1960s, the drug was put to therapeutic use to assist in the recovery of unconscious and repressed thoughts and feelings during psychotherapy. There was also military interest in the drug as a way of disabling enemy forces.

Following on from its therapeutic use, in the early 1960s in America and later in the UK, LSD began to be publicised and used for non-medical purposes. Among fringe and hippy groups it was seen as a key to quasi-religious transcendental experiences. Although LSD has been largely associated with the 1960s, use of the drug continued among certain unconventional groups throughout the 1970s and 1980s. With the advent of 'dance culture', LSD found a whole new market among young people attending raves and discos who might also be using amphetamine and ecstasy.

One dose may be sufficient for a mild 'trip', three or four would induce a full-blown hallucinogenic experience, depending on the strength of the tablet. The drug is usually sold impregnated into squares of blotting paper, known as tabs, carrying various colourful designs or images from popular culture (e.g. Batman, Bart Simpson and Sonic the Hedgehog). Tabs are dissolved under the tongue.

> ...and you couldn't put it into words. The White Smocks like to put it into words, like hallucination and dissociative phenomena. They could understand the visual skyrockets ... But the visual stuff was usually just the décor with LSD ... the whole thing was... the experience ... this certain indescribable feeling.
>
> Tom Wolfe, *The Electric Kool-Aid Acid Test*, Farrar, Strous, Giroux, 1968

PRICE

Tablets containing LSD cost £2.50–£3 each.

SHORT-TERM USE

A trip begins about half an hour to one hour after taking LSD, peaks after two to six hours and fades out after about 12 hours, depending on the dose, characteristically having progressed through several phases. The experience is hard to describe, partly because experiences differ, but also because they can be so much at variance with our accustomed ways of seeing the world.

Users report visual effects such as intensified colours, distorted shapes and sizes, and movement in stationary objects. Distortions of hearing occur, as do changes in sense of time and place. Generally, the user knows these effects to be unreal. True hallucinations are relatively rare. Physical effects are so slight compared with psychological or emotional effects that they are of little importance.

Emotional reactions vary, but include heightened self-awareness and mystical or ecstatic experiences. Feelings of dissociation from the body are commonly reported. Unpleasant reactions are more likely if the user is unstable, anxious or depressed and may include anxiety, depression, dizziness, disorientation, and sometimes a short-lived psychotic episode including hallucinations and paranoia.

The same person may have good and bad 'trips' on different occasions, and even within the same trip. But while the LSD experience is variable compared with most other drugs, it is also relatively more open to the user's intentions and to the suggestions of others. Hence, friendly reassurance is an effective antidote to a bad trip. Experienced users steer the trip towards the area they wish to experience or explore.

It is difficult to combine a trip with a task requiring concentration, and driving will almost certainly be impaired. Suicides or deaths due to LSD-induced beliefs or perceptions, though much publicised, are rare. Just one case of fatal overdose has been reported in the literature.

LONG-TERM USE

There are no known physical dangers attributable to long-term LSD use. In particular, there is no reliable evidence that LSD causes brain damage or damage to future children. Adverse psychological effects are possible after one trip, but are more common in regular users. Prolonged, serious psychological reactions are rare, but have been reported. These can be psychotic in nature and generally occur among individuals with existing or latent mental illness, most commonly after repeated LSD use.

A substantial minority of LSD users report short-lived, vivid re-experiences of part of a previous trip, again, especially after frequent use. These can leave the person feeling disorientated, anxious and distressed, but are rarely dangerous.

There is no physical dependence, and tolerance develops very rapidly so that after three or four days' use, further doses are ineffective unless the user abstains for a further three or four days. A small minority of those who use LSD become psychologically dependent.

Hallucinogenic mushrooms

A bewildering array of hallucinogenic plants were used by ancient tribes and civilisations (and many still are used by their successors), generally as a means of visionary divination and to gain access to the 'spirit' world. In the British Isles, the greatest current interest is in the dozen or so hallucinogenic fungi that grow here, notably the Amanita muscaria and the mushrooms of the Paneolus and Psilocybe families, especially Psilocybe semilanceata, the Liberty Cap or the magic mushroom.

Distinguishing hallucinogenic mushrooms from poisonous and sometimes deadly cousins is a complex skill, requiring reference to relevant botanical texts and some expertise in mushroom taxonomy.

LEGAL STATUS

There is no law pertinent to the harvesting, preparation or use of Amanita muscaria.

The position with respect to species containing psilocin and psilocybin is more complex. Ordinarily, these drugs are controlled under Class A of the Misuse of Drugs Act, and under regulations that prohibit their medical use. Their possession, production or supply, or the act of allowing premises to be used for their production or supply, are offences, unless in accordance with a Home Office licence issued for research or other special purposes.

However, while they are in the mushrooms, the drugs are not illegal until you do something like boiling or crushing the mushrooms, to make what is known as a 'preparation or other product' containing psilocin or psilocybin. Such a preparation is a controlled substance, subject to the same restrictions and penalties as the drugs it contains. How much one has to do to the mushroom to cross the border into illegality is unsure, but merely crushing them can be considered enough by the courts.

PRODUCTION AND SUPPLY

All of the mushrooms discussed here can be found wild in most parts of the UK. They prefer moist, often dark areas, usually in fields or, in the case of the Fly Agaric, near birch trees. The mushrooms grow in autumn, usually between August and October, particularly after periods of heavy rainfall. Parts of Wales, and northern England and Scotland yield large crops of the mushrooms during this period. The mushrooms are often dried and kept for later use or passed onto friends or buyers. Because of their availability, there is no significant black market in mushrooms. A number of varieties, such as Cubensis Mexicana, not native to the UK or Europe, are available in some speciality shops in countries such as Holland, but not in the UK. They may be grown or brought into the UK.

PREVALENCE

Among what are sometimes described as 'hippies', and among groups of teenagers, hallucinogenic mushroom eating has been reported as a common event in urban areas in Great Britain, and in rural Wales, particularly during harvest months. Surveys suggest that for the UK as a whole, about 1% of school children have tried magic mushrooms.

LICIT AND ILLICIT USE

Amanita muscaria (Fly Agaric) is still used by the ritual medicine men or 'shamans' of north-east Asia, Siberia, and even North America. The source of its hallucinogenic properties is likely to be muscimole, a chemical whose concentration is increased with the drying of the mushroom.

Psychoactive mushrooms of the Panealus and Psilocybe families contain the hallucinogens psilocybin and psilocin. These and other psilocybin mushrooms were sacred intoxicants among the Aztecs of Mexico at the time of the Spanish invasion in the 1500s. Psilocybin mushrooms may be eaten fresh or cooked, or brewed into a tea. They may also be preserved by drying.

In contrast, psilocybin mushrooms do not feature in European history, though pagan witchcraft was

> The sacred mushroom takes me by the hand and brings me to the world where everything is known. It is they, the sacred mushrooms, that speak in a way that I can understand.
>
> Shaman quoted in R.E. Schultes and A. Hoffman, *Plants of the Gods*, Hutchinson, 1979

> I am frequently asked why I do not reach for mushrooms every night. But ecstasy is not fun. In our everyday existence we divide experiences into good and bad ... There is a third category ecstasy that for most of us hovers off stage, a stranger we never meet. The hallucinogenic mushroom introduces ecstasy to us. Your very soul is seized and shaken until it tingles, until you fear you will never recover your equilibrium.
>
> R Gordon Wasson, pioneer of modern day research into mushrooms and shamanism, quoted in Gossop, *Living with Drugs*, 5th edition, Ashgate, 2000

associated with hallucinogens from the potato family, such as deadly nightshade and henbane. Present-day use of plant hallucinogens in the UK appears to have developed in the late 1970s as a legal and more 'organic' alternative to LSD.

The Liberty Cap (containing psilocybin) seems the most commonly occurring and most commonly used of the available species. It also seems the most consistently potent. It fruits between September and November throughout the UK. The mushroom is apparently pleasant tasting and does not generally cause potentially deterrent side-effects, though very similar-looking species can cause illness, and other species which might be confused with the Liberty Cap could be fatal, such as the Death Cap.

Amanita muscaria, too, is very common in early autumn, but unpleasant side-effects and the dangers and likelihood of mistaken identity should reduce its practical 'availability' for most potential users.

PRICE

Mushrooms are not dealt with in the black market to any great extent. Indications show that quantities of around 30 mushrooms, if and when they are sold, sell for around £5 a bag. These prices are merely indicative and do not represent a recognised street price.

SHORT-TERM USE

The effects of psilocybin-containing mushrooms are similar to a mild LSD experience, and the relevant comments about the variability of the experience and its susceptibility to the user's mood, environment and intentions all apply. Variability also arises from differences in potency of different samples of mushrooms and methods of preparation.

Like LSD the effects include euphoria and hilarity; however, other effects include physiological arousal (increased heart rate, blood pressure and pupil size). The effects also come on quicker (generally after about half an hour, peaking by about three hours) and last for a shorter time (four to nine hours – longer with higher doses). At low doses, euphoria and detachment predominate; at higher doses, visual distortions progress to vivid 'pseudohallucinations' of colour and movement. There are commonly feelings of nausea, vomiting and stomach pains, effects often attributed to the Fly Agaric which is similarly hallucinogenic, albeit more intense and introspective. The Fly Agaric is also associated more with drowsiness followed by a stimulation of the senses. Users of the Siberian north also talk of its ability to prolong physical endurance, possibly related to a heightening of the senses.

Infrequently (but especially after repeated or unusually high doses, if the user is inexperienced, or if they are anxious or unhappy to start with) 'bad trips' characterised by deep fear and anxiety can occur, and may develop into a psychotic episode. These can usually be dealt with by friendly reassurance and leave no persistent effects, though there have been reports of longer-lasting disturbances, such as recurrent anxiety attacks and 'flashbacks' to the original experience. Again, after a time, these almost invariably fade of their own accord.

But by far the greatest potential dangers arise from the possibility (in Britain) of picking poisonous Amanita species by mistake. Eating varieties such as Amanita phalloides or Amanita virosa can be fatal even when taken in small amounts. In contrast, it would take large amounts of Liberty Cap or Fly Agaric mushrooms to cause a fatal overdose. Reports of the correct dosage for the Fly Agaric vary, with reports of experienced users eating up to seven caps without illness (some have died from consuming considerably less). One to two caps, though is thought to be enough to bring on a strong hallucinatory experience. However, fatal poisoning due to mistaken identity has not yet been confirmed in Britain.

Mixing with other drugs

Mushrooms – because they are seasonal – tend to be taken on their own on an irregular basis. Similarly, users tend to be teenagers experimenting with drugs, usually one at a time. If taken with another drug, which is usually alcohol or cannabis, effects are unpredictable. Alcohol will usually exaggerate feelings of confusion and disorientation, whilst cannabis may enhance the intensity of the hallucinatory experience.

LONG-TERM USE

Like LSD, tolerance develops rapidly and the next day it might take twice as many Liberty Caps to repeat the experience. Full sensitivity is restored after about a week, so there is a natural discouragement to daily use. There are no significant withdrawal symptoms and no physical dependence, though, of course, individuals may become psychologically attached and feel a desire to repeat their experiences. At present, no serious lasting sequels to the long-term use of hallucinogenic mushrooms have been reported, but there are no studies which might permit an assessment of the effects of extended, frequent use.

Ecstasy

Ecstasy or MDMA, known on the streets as 'E' and many other names derived from the shape and colour of the various formulations, is classed as a hallucinogenic amphetamine, a group of drugs with effects roughly combining those of amphetamine and LSD.

LEGAL STATUS

As with LSD, the drug 'leaked out' into the general population and was eventually banned in America in 1985. In the late 1960s concern in this country about the proliferation of hallucinogenic amphetamines in America prompted the banning of specific drugs such as MDA and TMA. But after a raid on a laboratory in the mid-1970s, a drug of this type not covered by the legislation was discovered, plus the formulae for others. So, in 1977, an amendment to the Misuse of Drugs Act was introduced, designed to cover all amphetamine-like compounds including MDMA.

Ecstasy is a Class A drug. No doctor can prescribe it and anybody wanting to use it for research purposes has to obtain a licence from the Home Office.

PRODUCTION AND SUPPLY

Ecstasy is part of a group of drugs in the MDA family. Some of these drugs, including ecstasy, are derived from the oils of natural products such as nutmeg and sassafras oil. Others, like PMA and DOM are entirely synthetic and are very much stronger. MDMA is produced in underground labs, particularly in Holland, but also in parts of Eastern Europe. Large quantities of the drug also appear to be produced in Asia, especially in India and Thailand.

Sold usually as tablets, known as pills, or in capsules, they can take various shapes and colours, often stamped with motifs such as the Mitsubishi car logo. Less commonly, the drug is also available as a powder. In an attempt to maximise profits, some tablets sold as ecstasy contain little or none of the drug at all, but might be concoctions of drugs such as amphetamine, LSD or ketamine.

PREVALENCE

Trying to estimate the numbers of ecstasy users has proved difficult. Use of the drug soared in the 1990s, with figures of one million users a week bandied about with little basis in evidence. According to the British Crime Survey, use of the drug may have fallen in some parts of the UK, but figures from other sources suggest that while use may not be escalating at the previous rate, nonetheless, use remains high among those who frequent the club scene. Currently, it is estimated that 700,000–800,000 people have used ecstasy in the past year.

LICIT AND ILLICIT USE

MDMA was first synthesised in 1912, but no medical or commercial use could be found for it until marital therapists in America discovered its potential for encouraging empathy between clients, diffusing anger and hostility.

Ecstasy has been available in this country since the mid-1980s, but only in any quantity since 1988 when it was strongly associated with Acid House music and the parties at which it was played. Since then, the drug has become more widespread among young people not necessarily connected with the music scene. Because of its stimulant properties, the drug is usually used socially where the user wishes to stay up all night long.

One or two ecstasy tablets is the normal dose at dance events or similar. It is not unknown for users to take up to seven or more in the space of a whole night and day. The drug is usually taken orally, but it may also be snorted, and even sprinkled into joints and smoked.

PRICE

The price has fallen dramatically as ecstasy has become a regular part of the UK drug scene. Ecstasy is sold in a wide variety of capsules and tablets of differing shape and colour for anything between £2.50–£7 a tablet depending on the locality and strength.

SHORT-TERM USE

MDMA is effective at the moderate single dose level of 75–100mg; effects are experienced after 20–60 minutes and can last several hours. Pupils become dilated, the jaw tightens and there is usually brief nausea, sweating, dry mouth and throat, some rise in blood pressure and heart rate, and loss of appetite. There can be some difficulty with bodily co-ordination making it potentially dangerous to drive or operate machinery under the influence of MDMA. At doses above 200mg or if the drug is being used repeatedly over a few days, all these effects may be experienced more acutely.

Once the drug is stopped, there may be some residual effects similar to those experienced by amphetamine users, including fatigue and depression which can last for several days.

Over 100 deaths directly associated with the effects of taking ecstasy have been recorded in otherwise apparently healthy young people. With a few exceptions, all these young people collapsed at raves or shortly afterwards and all exhibited symptoms associated with severe heatstroke. Using ecstasy produces similar symptoms, and the current best guess is that these users have succumbed to the cumulative effects of taking MDMA while dancing for long periods of time in a very hot, humid atmosphere. However, there is no evidence to show why these particular individuals have died. In a few rare cases, individuals have died through excess of water intake in the belief that this would protect from the side-effects of ecstasy. Research suggests that because women retain fluid more readily than men, they may be more at risk in this respect.

As with LSD, whether the experience is 'bad' or 'good' often depends on what mood the user is in before the drug is taken, what the user expects to happen and the friendliness or otherwise of the immediate surroundings.

At moderate dose levels, most users report a mild euphoric 'rush' followed by feelings of serenity and calmness and the dissipation of anger and hostility. The drug appears to stimulate empathy between users, but there is no conclusive proof that ecstasy is an aphrodisiac; it tends to enhance the sensual experience of sex rather than stimulate the desire for sexual activity or increase sexual excitement. MDMA also inhibits orgasm in men and women and may inhibit male erection. Even so, concerns that the use of the drug could undermine 'safe sex' practices, with implications for the spread of HIV, may be valid.

At moderate dose levels, there is heightened perception of surroundings without the visual distortions and illusions associated with LSD – thus MDMA is to some extent 'psychedelic' viz 'mind expanding' without being hallucinogenic. However, some particularly sensitive individuals may experience visual imagery, particularly in 'the mind's eye', when the eyes are closed and hallucinations have been reported at higher dose levels. One of the residual effects of MDMA, after a 'run' of using the drug for a few days, may be 'flashbacks'. This is a well-documented after-effect of using LSD, where the LSD 'trip' is briefly relived some time after the event, causing anxiety and confusion. Drugs sold as ecstasy but which are not, such as MDA and MDEA, have slightly different effects to MDMA, and could possibly be the source of many bad trips associated with ecstasy use. MDA, for example, is said to have a stronger hallucinatory effect, often bringing on nausea, and is less euphoric, particularly in high doses.

Most of the bad experiences with the drug have been reported by those using higher doses over a period of time and include anxiety, panic, confusion, insomnia, psychosis, and visual and auditory hallucinations. Generally, these effects remit once the drug is stopped, but can leave the user in a weakened mental and physical condition for a while. Some of these effects have been experienced by those who have tried the drug for 'self-therapy' and have then been unable to deal with the emotions that using MDMA has brought to the surface.

Mixing with other drugs

Ecstasy is often mixed with a number of drugs such as amphetamine, cocaine, cannabis, LSD and 2CB. These drugs are usually taken to enhance or prolong the stimulant effects, as is the case for amphetamine and cocaine. Others such as cannabis are used to cushion the drug come down. Alcohol is generally not taken at the same time as ecstasy. Alcohol tends to dehydrate the body, an effect most users choose to avoid.

LONG-TERM USE

Some long-term users have reported increased susceptibility to minor ailments such as colds, flu and sore throats. One researcher has observed that for unknown reasons, MDA seems to be especially hard on women and will activate any latent infections or problems in the female genito-urinary tract. Although the evidence is highly circumstantial, it may be that the MDA group of drugs adversely affects the immune system.

There have been indications of liver damage, but it is unclear whether this is simply a more immediate consequence of heatstroke, or due to toxicity over the longer term.

Tolerance develops to the effects of MDMA, but there is no physical dependence, no heroin-like withdrawal symptoms, nor any evidence that MDMA is used compulsively on a long-term basis.

Researchers agree that the drug depletes levels of serotonin in the brain. Among other things, serotonin is the chemical which helps regulate mood; reducing serotonin levels would account for the mid-week blues reported by many users. Researchers also agree that ecstasy reduces the density of neurons in the brain, as evidenced by brain-scan images. However, there is no agreement that these effects of the drug constitute irreversible 'brain damage' that will impact on the user in years to come. No attempt has been made to interpret the results from a behavioural point of view. Extrapolations from research into the neurotoxicity of ecstasy – including indications of memory loss and other cognitive problems – remain speculative.

SPECIAL CASES

Research suggests that individuals suffering from heart disease, high blood pressure, glaucoma, epilepsy, or those with a mental condition, should avoid ecstasy use. There is no evidence as yet that the drug has any effect on the foetus or causes problems to the newborn. Women with a history of genito-urinary tract infection should not use the drug.

Anabolic steroids

Anabolic steroids are one group of hormones that occur naturally in the body and are responsible for the development and functioning of the reproductive organs. In the male, the hormone produced in the largest quantity is testosterone. As well as controlling the growth, development and function of the male sex organs, this hormone is also responsible for masculine characteristics such as the growth of body hair and the deeper voice. Anabolic steroids also have an 'anabolic' or building up effect on the body in that they promote the build-up of muscle tissue. Most of the synthetic anabolic steroids on the market are derived from testosterone.

Medically, anabolic steroids have limited uses in the treatment of anaemia, trauma patients (burns, surgery, radiation therapy) and patients with chronic muscle-wasting illnesses such as AIDS. They are also used to treat hormonal dysfunction, and are increasingly being considered for impotence and male hormone replacement treatment.

LEGAL STATUS

Anabolic steroids are Prescription Only drugs under the 1968 Medicines Act. They can only be sold by a pharmacist working from a registered pharmacy and then only on the presentation of a doctor's prescription. Anabolic steroids are also controlled under Class C of the Misuse of Drugs Act whereby it is illegal to supply the drugs, but not illegal to possess them for personal use.

PRODUCTION AND SUPPLY

There are a bewildering number of steroids available; some are diverted pharmaceutical products, some are illicitly produced, while others are for veterinary use only. Most are distributed through public gymnasia, body-building clubs and the like. Common types include nandrolone, stanozolol and testosterone sold under various trade names. Many illicitly available steroids are counterfeit and vary in potency and may not even contain much of what they are claimed to contain.

PREVALENCE

According to the 2001 British Crime Survey, between 12,000–42,000 people aged 16–59 said they have used anabolic steroids in the previous year, with the best estimate at 23,000. Among those aged 16–24, the best estimate of those who have used in the past year is 11,000.

Use is often localised and specific to young people who use it either for cosmetic or performance reasons. It is therefore often found among gym users and other high performance sports enthusiasts, though not exclusively. A survey of needle exchanges in Merseyside, 1998–2001, saw the number of new steroid clients presenting for clean works rise from 398 to 558, meaning they now outnumbered new opiate using clients. Other needle exchange schemes similarly report high numbers of steroid-using clients.

LICIT AND ILLICIT USE

Steroids can be taken orally or injected. As used by athletes and bodybuilders, these drugs are taken in multiple combinations over cycles of six-eight weeks, in dosages far in excess of therapeutic recommendations.

PRICE

The average cost of a steroid 'cycle' has been reported at between £70 £140, with an annual cost of buying steroids put at between £500–£2,500 a year.

SHORT-TERM USE

During the periods of use, users report that steroids make them feel more aggressive, such that they train harder, and that using steroids also helps them recover more quickly from strenuous exercise. Feelings of aggression from using steroids are likely to be felt in about 24 hours, if at all. Some researchers have suggested this is only a placebo effect. However, in laboratory studies, those used to taking steroids have been able to tell whether they have been given the drug or just a placebo. There is some controversy over the phenomenon known as 'road rage'. It is claimed that otherwise placid individuals have been driven to acts of extreme violence by their use of steroids. This is countered by the view that only those who had violent and aggressive tendencies in the first place would be thus affected. Three-quarters of steroid users are said to experience some kind of aggressive tendencies.

Stop being skinny and one of the crowd. Have you ever wanted to walk into a club and be worshipped by the masses and take your pick of sexual partners. Then join us, for this is the reality for me and some of our friends. Join us.

When you hear about steroid users getting into fights because of drugs, they are mainly idiots. They are the idiots of society who want to cause trouble and steroids allow them to become even bigger idiots.

Both quoted in P. Korkia and G.V. Stimson, 'Anabolic Steroid Use in Great Britain', Centre for Research of Drugs and Health Behaviour, 1993

Equally controversial is the question as to whether steroids enhance athletic performance. Where the user is already undergoing intensive training and a specialised diet regime, taking steroids will build up lean as well as total body mass and increase the size of muscles. This is why these drugs are popular among bodybuilders. However, the evidence that they increase muscle strength as well is inconclusive. Even so, it is clear that many athletes and coaches are convinced of their direct efficacy in improving performance alongside their ability to promote more aggressive training, which of itself could bring results. It must also be borne in mind that all national and international sporting organisations have banned the use of these drugs and a whole range of other 'performance enhancing' drugs on the grounds of cheating.

LONG-TERM USE

As users often take steroids in multiple combinations and at doses that would be unethical to replicate in a clinical test, it is difficult to make conclusive statements about the long-term effects of using these drugs. The available evidence shows that:

- liver function tests can show abnormalities when steroids are being used, but return to normal once use of the drug has stopped. A rare form of hepatitis is also associated with steroid use. Among regular, heavy users of steroids isolated cases of liver tumours have been reported together with cancer of the kidney, which is normally very rare in adults;

- steroids may cause hypertension because they encourage the body to retain water, which raises blood pressure;

- users who inject with dirty (non- sterile) equipment run the risk of contracting HIV;

- steroids can affect growth in young people by causing early fusion of the cartilage plates at the ends of the bones;

- in men, the reproductive and hormonal systems are affected. Because of the presence of steroids, the body's natural production of testosterone is lowered. Sperm output and quality is decreased and may take some months to return to normal. Sex drive may increase at first and then become depressed until use is stopped. Some men may also show over-development of breasts that may not be reversible except by surgery. This would only happen in rare cases and with only those types of anabolic steroids that convert to female oestrogen hormone in the body;

- women report increased sex drive and the clitoris may become enlarged, neither of which are necessarily undesirable effects for some women;

- women users run the risk of developing secondary male sexual characteristics such as growth of facial and body hair, deepening of the voice and a decrease in breast size, all of which appear to be irreversible. These characteristics may be passed on to a female foetus if the woman is pregnant while taking the drugs;

- there have been some cases of temporary psychiatric problems such as confusion, sleep disorders, depression and paranoia which abate after steroid use has stopped. The defence of 'steroid mania' has been used recently on behalf of those accused of violent crimes;

- as with any coping mechanism, there may be psychological dependence with steroids, if the user is convinced that they perform better while on the drugs. Athletes have reported lethargy and depression after stopping steroids and some may continue use rather than face these symptoms.

Alcohol

Alcoholic drinks chiefly consist of water and ethyl alcohol (or 'ethanol'), produced by the fermentation of fruits, vegetables or grain. Beer is about one part ethanol to 20 parts water, wine is about twice to four times as strong, and distilled spirits such as whisky, rum and gin consist of almost half ethanol, the rest water.

Below is some information on the relative strengths of various kinds of alcoholic drinks. The term 'ABV' means 'alcohol by volume' or what percentage of the total liquid is actually alcohol.

Alcopops

Most of these have an ABV of 4–5.5% with a range of units from 1.5–1.8 per bottle, with Thunderbird at 13.1%. The most well-known brands are the alcoholic lemonades and there are also alcoholic colas, fruit-flavoured drinks and those using spirits such as vodka and tequila.

Cider

This varies in strength from the low alcohol varieties such as Strongbow LA with an ABV of just 0.9%, up to the 'white ciders' with an ABV of around 8.4%. Bottles usually contain 330ml; cans 440ml. A can of one of the stronger ciders contains around 2.5–3.5 units of alcohol.

Spirits

Most standard 700ml bottles of whisky, vodka or rum have an ABV of around 40% containing 25–30 units of alcohol.

Wine

Most wines are produced with an ABV of around 10–13%, in a standard 750ml bottle containing 9–10 units of alcohol. Wines from hotter climates (e.g. Italian and Californian wines are about 2–3% stronger than those from cooler climates (e.g. German wines). Australian wines tend to have the highest ABV values.

Sherry is usually produced with an ABV of 15–20%, giving around 13–14 units of alcohol for a typical 750ml bottle.

Beer and lager

Most popular types of bitter beer are around 3.5–4.1% ABV – giving around 2–2.25 units for a pint and 1.5 to 1.75 units for a 440ml can.

The strength of lager beers can vary widely and ranges from very low strength drinks like Barbican (0.02% ABV) to 'super strong' lagers, at anything up to 10%. But like bitter beers, many popular lagers are around 3.5–4% ABV, providing 1.5–1.75 units in a 440ml can and 2–2.25 units in a pint.

Beer and wine drinking almost certainly predate recorded history. For centuries 'ale-houses' and beer drinking have been a ubiquitous part of everyday life in Britain.

A different kind of alcohol, produced from wood (methyl alcohol), is used in methylated spirits and surgical spirit. Some down-and-out alcoholics ('meths' drinkers) drink these products because of their cheapness. Methyl alcohol is very poisonous and frequently causes blindness, coma and death from acidosis.

Unlike most of the other drugs in this guide, alcohol has food value in the sense that it supplies calories. One gram of alcohol supplies seven calories, compared to four calories from a gram of carbohydrate. A pint of beer can supply as many calories as six slices of bread. But beer provides very little vitamin or protein, and distilled spirits, none at all.

LEGAL STATUS

Concern to suppress gatherings of the lower classes, which might act as a focus for political agitation, lay behind the 1495 Act giving JPs powers to close troublesome ale-houses (something the Labour Government of today is proposing to re-introduce). Later laws regulated public drinking and, in the late nineteenth and early twentieth centuries, restricted young people's access to alcohol and the bar-rooms of pubs to prevent their being 'corrupted' by their elders. Restricted 'opening' hours were introduced in the First

> ...it provokes the desire, but takes away the performance.
> *MacBeth*

World War, to prevent drinking affecting the efficiency of war industries. Concern about unrest or 'over-indulgence' in the labouring classes and the competing fiscal benefits of the alcohol traffic were behind much of public policy.

The manufacture, sale, purchase and distribution of alcoholic beverages are controlled by licensing regulations. There are no laws against possessing or drinking alcohol, except that under the Public Order Act 1986, it is an offence to carry or possess alcohol on trains, coaches or minibuses travelling to and from designated sporting events. Some cities have introduced by-laws prohibiting public consumption in city centre areas. Licensing regulations limit where alcohol can be sold to those premises licensed by local authorities. Generally, pubs and other licensed premises may be open 24 hours a day. Off-licences can open between 8am and 11pm.

There are graduated restrictions with respect to age. No child under 16 years old is allowed in licensed premises unaccompanied. It is an offence to give alcohol to a child under five. In Northern Ireland it is an offence for people under 18 to enter licensed premises. Elsewhere, children of any age can enter parts of licensed premises, including the bar, where the landlord has requested a special licence (although children must leave the bar area by 9pm); children can also be in the pub garden and (other than in Scotland) can be bought alcohol to drink there, providing they are over five years of age. At 14, children can enter the bar (the place where alcohol is bought and consumed) of licensed premises, but not until 18 can they drink alcohol there. It is also at 18 years that the teenager can legally purchase alcohol in a pub or from an off-licence. The main exception is the provision allowing 16-year-olds to buy beer, cider or perry (and in Scotland wine), but only to drink with a meal not served at a bar. In some areas it is a local offence to consume alcohol in public. Glasgow and Lambeth in London are two examples where, because of perceived public unrest, public drinking is prohibited.

It is an offence to be drunk in a public place – including licensed premises – to be drunk and disorderly, or to drive while unfit to do so because of drink. More precisely, it is also an offence to drive with more than 80mg of alcohol in every 100ml of blood.

Unlicensed 'home-brewing' of beers, wines and cider (not spirits) is permitted, but the products cannot be sold.

PRODUCTION AND SUPPLY

Nearly all alcohol is produced in large brewery and distillery chains. The UK also imports large quantities of beer, wine and spirits from Europe and other areas of the world.

Alcohol is retailed by on-licence outlets, that is to say pubs owned by many breweries, multiple pub operators or independent operators, who sell alcohol for consumption on their premises. Alcohol is also available on an off-licence basis from grocers/supermarkets and specialist off-licences which are authorised to sell alcohol for consumption off the premises only.

There are currently more than 80,000 pubs and the alike in the UK, over 50,000 off-licences (an increasing proportion of which are in supermarkets), plus a further 40,000 licensed premises such as restaurants or clubs.

With beers and wines much cheaper on the continent, a great deal is being imported from France and Belgium and privately consumed or sold on to shops and bars. This is thought to cost the taxpayer £185 million in revenue and retailers more than double this in revenue, particularly near to the ports in the South-East. However, this is completely overshadowed by the government forecast for alcohol duty receipts in 2003 at £113 billion.

> I like alcohol. It is a powerful drug and, God knows, for some people a hellish one, but if used carefully it can give great pleasure. After a long, hard day, the splendid warm glow that strong drink provides is one of my favourite feelings.
>
> Quoted in A. Weil and W. Rosen, *From Chocolate to Morphine*, Haughton Mifflin Company, 1998

Alcohol

The government's advice on sensible drinking has in recent years been for men to drink no more than 21 units, and women no more than 14 units, a week.
It is now considered more helpful to view this guidance in daily terms and is therefore recommended that one unit of alcohol is equivalent to:

half a pint of average strength beer, cider or lager
1 single pub measure of spirits
1 small glass of wine
1 small glass of sherry

PREVALENCE

Over 90% of the adult population drink to a greater or lesser extent. Drinking starts at an early age in this country. It has been estimated that almost 90% of boys in England have drunk alcohol by the age of 13. Despite the licensing laws, around 60% of children aged between 13 and 17 are likely to have bought alcohol in a pub or off-licence. In the 13–16 years age range, about a third of children drink at least once a week, but mostly in the home and generally in small amounts.

On average men drinkers consume the equivalent of about one and a half pint of beer a day, women about half pint. One in five men drink three and a half to four pints or more at least once a week.

LICIT AND ILLICIT USE

Getting drunk is a relatively common event. On their own admission, nearly half the male population and one in seven women will have been drunk in the last three months. Younger age groups drink more. In the late teens and early twenties, alcohol consumption is 40–50% above average and along with this goes a higher incidence of being drunk and of heavier drinking.

Voluntary advertising restrictions are less stringent than with tobacco. Spirits are not advertised on TV, and adverts are not allowed to be directed at youngsters, link drink and driving, or encourage excessive use. However, much of English football is sponsored by alcohol manufacturers and there has been a recent trend in producing 'designer' drinks aimed at young people, including ciders, lagers and alcoholic lemonade, in a possible attempt to win back young people from 'dance drugs' such as ecstasy. This can generally be seen as successful in that by contrast to the early days of the rave scene, alcohol is now regularly available in most clubs and dance venues.

PRICE

Alcohol prices vary regionally and from retailer to retailer. A pound will typically buy one unit of alcohol. Compared to other drugs, alcohol often costs more in terms of units of consumption. As little as £1.50 of cannabis resin, for example, can make a potent enough joint to last two or three smokers an hour or so of intoxication. A pint of strong lager in comparison may cost up to £2.50 for one person, lasting at most half an hour of drinking. A typical user of ecstasy, for example, may spend £10 for a whole night of clubbing, the equivalent cost of three to four pints of beer.

SHORT–TERM USE

Alcohol is absorbed into the bloodstream and starts to have an effect within five or ten minutes, lasting up to several hours, depending on dose. How much effect a drink has, depends on its strength and how quickly it is drunk, whether there is food in the stomach, and the body weight and mood of the drinker. Since tolerance develops, the effects will also depend on how much the person is used to drinking.

After the equivalent of about two pints of beer, most people would feel less inhibited and more relaxed. Emotional reactions range from jovial to aggressive, depending on the circumstances, and the efficiency of mental and physical functioning is reduced. After another two pints, drinkers generally become rather unco-ordinated and slur their words a little: emotional reactions can become highly exaggerated and variable. More drinks might result in staggering, double vision and loss of balance, followed by unconsciousness. (These effects may be compared with those of barbiturates.) Generally, people try to take enough alcohol to feel pleasantly relaxed, and not so much as to lose control of themselves.

Mixing with other drugs

Alcohol more than any drug is used in conjunction with other substances. Alcohol exaggerates the effects of other drugs which depress the nervous system. Taken with benzodiazepines or barbiturates, for example, it produces a very drunken-like state, which can result in unconsciousness and possibly overdose. Vomiting whilst unconscious is also a common cause of drug-related deaths. Similar effects are common if drunk with opiates, antihistamines, solvents and cannabis.

LONG-TERM USE

As with most drugs, effects are related to dose, and some of the extreme forms of physical damage, such as liver cirrhosis are only commonly seen after substantial tolerance has developed and the individual has become heavily dependent ('alcoholic'). Damage may occur as a direct effect of alcohol in the body, or because of the lifestyle associated with/encouraged by heavy drinking. For instance, alcohol supplies calories but no other dietary essentials, so heavy drinking encourages obesity with its attendant dangers and an inadequate diet with consequent protein and vitamin deficiencies. In alcoholics, these dietary deficiencies allied with stomach and liver disorders can result in incapacitating brain damage.

Excessive drinking commonly aggravates family, personal and financial problems, sometimes contributing to family breakdown, or to repeated violence and other forms of crime associated with a loss of self-control.

Sudden withdrawal from heavy use of alcohol produces sweating, anxiety, trembling and delirium (the 'DTs'). It can even result in convulsions, coma and death.

SPECIAL CASES

Women drinking six units or more a day while pregnant may give birth to babies with withdrawal symptoms, facial abnormalities and lasting retardation of physical and mental development. Cases of this 'foetal alcohol syndrome' are rare in Britain. Lesser degrees of regular drinking may result in less serious effects such as lowered birth-weight, but there is little evidence that moderate drinking (say, up to two units a day) causes significant harm to mother or baby.

Caffeine

The most ubiquitous of the stimulants is caffeine, found in coffee, tea and soft drinks, and in over-the-counter analgesics and headache pills.

Coffee is the strongest of the beverages; one strong cup of 'real' coffee may contain caffeine equivalent to the minimal stimulant dose. Coffee was introduced into England in 1601 and popularised on medical grounds. Later 'coffee shops' spread as a forum for male social and political activities, provoking governmental licensing restrictions and suppression.

A cup of tea generally contains less, but can contain almost as much caffeine as instant coffee. It comes from the dried leaves of a shrub native to South-East Asia and was introduced into Britain, again as a medicine, in 1661, but soon became popular as a 'pick-me-up'. Despite opposition, by the late 1700s tea had ousted coffee as the national beverage and had become one of the state's chief sources of revenue.

Soft drinks also generally contain less caffeine than coffee, but, because of their lower body weight, children consuming a full can could ingest the caffeine equivalent of four cups of coffee.

Caffeine itself is a white powder used as a mild stimulant in various preparations, though it is also used for some headaches and has diuretic properties.

LEGAL STATUS

Caffeine is not subject to any legal prohibitions on its manufacture, sale, distribution or possession.

Tonics containing caffeine such as Labiton are Pharmacy Only medicines, while some migraine treatments containing caffeine such as Migril are Prescription Only under the Medicines Act. Their sale is limited to a registered pharmacy in accordance with a prescription, though it is not illegal to possess them without a prescription, nor to give them away.

PRODUCTION AND SUPPLY

Coffee is made from the roasted beans of the tropical coffee bush, tea from the tea shrub. Caffeine is also found in other products such as cocoa beans and chocolate, some soft drinks and alcoholic beverages, and other herbs such as maté. Caffeinated beverages are sold without restriction in grocers and supermarkets, and employers make them available to their workforce during rest breaks. Each cup of brewed coffee provides an average 115mg (drip method) or 80mg (percolated) of caffeine, instant coffee about 65mg, tea 60mg, and a can or bottle of soft drink from 30 to 50mg, all with wide variations depending on the amount used and the method of preparation. These compare with the standard stimulant dose of 200mg.

Caffeine can also be bought on its own in the form of 'pep pills'. ProPlus is an example, available from chemists and most grocers.

PREVALENCE

Seventy per cent of all UK adults drink coffee and 86% drink tea. On average, each coffee drinker consumes over three cups a day, while per capita tea consumption averages over four cups a day. From these and other sources, daily caffeine consumption in Britain averages over 440mg per person, although given the explosion of coffee outlets selling strong coffee, this may now have increased.

LICIT AND ILLICIT USE

Offering tea or coffee is a customary form of hospitality to visitors, and there can hardly be a restaurant or café in the country that does not provide one or the other, or both. Caffeine pills are often taken as a 'keep me awake' pill, whilst driving, at work, or as a general stimulant.

> We have seen several well-marked cases of coffee excess ... The sufferer is tremulous, and loses his self-command; he is subject to fits of agitation and depression; he loses colour and has a haggard appearance. The appetite falls off, and symptoms of gastric catarrh may be manifested. The heart also suffers; it palpitates, or it intermits. As with other such agents, a renewed dose of the poison gives temporary relief, but at the cost of future misery.
>
> Sir T.C. Allbutt and H.D. Rolleston, *A System of Medicine*, 1909

> Far beyond all other pleasures, rarer than jewels or treasures, sweeter than grape from the vine. Yes! Yes! Greatest of pleasures! Coffee, coffee, how I love its flavour, and if you would win my favour, yes! Yes! Let me have coffee, let me have my coffee strong.
>
> From the *Coffee Cantata* by JS Bach

Students are renowned users of caffeine, in any form, to aid them through heavy study loads at exam times. With up to 50mg in each caffeine tablet, it would be easy for someone to add as much again to their caffeine consumption from beverages. Some athletes also allegedly use the drug as a legitimate performance enhancer, typically in the form of a caffeine suppository. Some regard the drug as a slimming aid, but there is evidence to suggest this is not the case. In the USA, for example, the drug has been banned as an additive to slimming products.

SHORT-TERM USE

Caffeine is an indirect nervous system stimulant in that it 'prevents' the brain from slowing down, therefore not actually stimulating the brain, just letting it function effectively. In moderate doses (150–250mg), the drug allays drowsiness and fatigue and postpones the onset of sleep, helping prevent boredom and tiredness interfering with performance on manual and intellectual tasks. Larger doses impair performance, especially where delicate co-ordination of movement is required. There are increased feelings of alertness, or sometimes of anxiety. Physiological effects can include increased heart rate, raised blood pressure, increased excretion of urine (these diminish with repeated use), constriction of blood vessels in the brain (relieving some types of headache) and increased breathing. Coffee – even decaffeinated coffee – increases stomach acidity.

Effects of coffee are evident within an hour, lasting three–four hours. Afterwards, there can be a 'let-down' effect of increased fatigue.

Excessive use

Consumption of 500–600mg of caffeine a day can cause feelings of anxiety and restlessness. After upwards of one gram of caffeine taken at one go (say 15 cups of instant coffee), the physiological effects may become pronounced enough to cause abnormally increased sensitivity and sensory disturbances (like ringing in the ear and light flashes), together with insomnia, muscle tremor, abnormally elevated heart rate and breathing, and gastrointestinal complaints such as nausea, vomiting and diarrhoea. Restlessness and excitement may progress to delirium. Death from overdose is possible but very unlikely and very rare (it would normally take over 100 cups of coffee).

LONG-TERM USE

People consuming the caffeine equivalent of seven or more cups of strong coffee a day may feel chronically anxious and irritable, and experience muscle tremor and headache. The stimulant effect may also cause chronic insomnia, but all these disturbances will clear up once caffeine intake is reduced.

Tolerance develops to many (but not all) of the physiological effects of caffeine, and there is a well-established withdrawal syndrome, noticeable after regular use of about 370mg a day. On discontinuing, the habitual user feels less alert and relaxed, more drowsy and irritable, and may experience headaches which can be severe. Regular drinkers often feel tired and irritable if they miss their usual morning coffee. Dependence, mainly psychological, can develop to the extent that people find it hard to stop drinking coffee, even for medical reasons.

Evidence that heavy, long-term coffee drinking increases the risk of peptic ulcer, heart disease or certain cancers is inconclusive, and adverse effects are likely to be infrequent and generally slight. However, individuals suffering from ulcers, high blood pressure or anxiety may find that excessive caffeine/coffee consumption aggravates their condition.

Tobacco

Tobacco is the dried leaves of the plant that grows in many parts of the world (it will even grow in England). The drug effect of tobacco is caused by nicotine, a mild stimulant found naturally only in tobacco leaves, which vaporises into the smoke when tobacco is burnt.

LEGAL STATUS

After tobacco was brought to England in the second half of the sixteenth century, there was a fierce dispute about its properties and benefits. But by 1625 tobacco's revenue advantages had led even King James – till then a fanatical opponent – to accept its widespread non-medical use and to regulate the trade in the interests of Britain's American colonies. Since then, tobacco's economic importance has tempered reaction to the medical consequences of its long-term use. However, the Food and Drug Administration in America has officially declared tobacco an addictive drug and is seeking controls under the drug laws.

The tobacco industry has in the past entered into voluntary agreements which detail codes of practice on tobacco advertising. These include clauses that cigarette advertising should not, for example, associate smoking with masculinity, virility, femininity, sexual success, achievement or courage, and it should not be aimed at young people, although it is this group which smokes the most heavily advertised brands. Cigarettes are not allowed to be advertised on television and, since 1991, this prohibition has been extended to other tobacco products such as pipe tobacco and cigars.

Since 2003, tobacco advertising and promotion are banned in the UK, following the passage of the Tobacco Advertising and Promotion Act in December 2002, and will also be banned throughout the European Union as a result of an EU Directive. The EU Directive is considerably weaker than the UK Act and only applies to cross-border advertising (e.g. by radio, internet) and sponsorship. It does not cover indirect advertising. However, the Directive permits EU member states to apply stronger measures so that a ban on indirect advertising will apply in the UK by virtue of the UK law. Under the terms of the UK Act, tobacco advertising in the print media and on billboards, and direct mail and other promotions, are prohibited. Britain is unlikely, however, to follow restrictions found in some US states which prohibit smoking from virtually all public places such as bars, restaurants or shopping centres.

Selling any tobacco products to children under 16 is prohibited. This prohibition was strengthened by the Children and Young Persons (Protection from Tobacco) Act 1991. Under this law, the maximum penalty for selling to those under 16 was increased from £400 to £2,500; all retailers selling tobacco have to prominently display a notice about not selling to children and local authorities now have a statutory obligation to monitor retail outlets selling tobacco.

There are few convictions for selling tobacco to under-16s, only 136 in 1999. In 1998, 22% of 11–15-year-olds were reported trying to buy cigarettes from a shop and, of these, only 40% were refused sales. Apart from this law, there are no restrictions on sale, other than that the import duty and other taxes should have been paid. Even though children cannot legally be sold tobacco, they can nevertheless legally buy, possess and smoke it.

Commercial manufacture of tobacco does require a licence, but if you wish, you can 'grow your own' with impunity.

The main legislative control over the availability of tobacco is exercised through the effect of taxation on price, obviously a factor in how much will be bought and by whom. Currently taxes account for around 80% of the price of a typical packet of 20 cigarettes.

PREVALENCE

The smoking habit starts early, particularly for girls. A quarter of 15-year-old girls and one-fifth of boys, are regular smokers. About 30% of older teenagers smoke, each smoker consuming on average ten cigarettes a day.

Every 10 seconds, another person dies as a result of tobacco use. Tobacco products are estimated to have caused around 3 million deaths a year in the early 1990s. The death toll is steadily increasing and, unless current trends are reversed, that figure is expected to rise to 10 million deaths per year by the 2020s or early 2030s, with 70% of those deaths occurring in developing countries.

The World Health Organisation, *Tobacco or Health: A Global Status Report*, 1997

Below retirement age, the percentage of women cigarette smokers is only a few per cent below the figure for men, though if pipe and cigar smoking is included the percentage difference increases, with 33% of men smoking as opposed to 26% of women.

LICIT USE

Tobacco is consumed as a mild stimulant by just over a quarter of the adult population. Users smoke the drug as a relaxant on most occasions, though most smokers say they are more likely to light up in the company of others who do likewise. Many use the drug regularly, with nearly one in ten men and one in twelve women smoking sufficiently (20+ cigarettes a day) to be classed as heavy smokers. Many find the habit difficult to stop because of its addictive properties and because of its appetite suppressant qualities which, it is suggested, make the drug attractive to many women (and men) concerned about their weight. There are 13 million ex-smokers in the UK.

Tobacco is often used in making cannabis cigarettes or joints. Both rolling tobacco and tobacco removed from packet cigarettes are mixed with resin or herbal cannabis and rolled into cigarette papers. Longer types of cigarette papers are often used to make sufficiently large joints to pass among friends.

PRICE

The price of cigarettes is determined by the level of taxation, currently about 80% of the retail price. In 2003, for example, the average price of a packet of 20 cigarettes was £4.20, of which £3.29 went to the Inland Revenue, raising a total of around £10 million for the Treasury.

SHORT-TERM USE

Cigarette smoke consists of droplets of tar, nicotine, carbon monoxide and other gases. Nicotine and other substances are absorbed by the lungs, so how much is absorbed depends on how much smoke is actually inhaled rather than 'puffed'.

Nicotine is a drug with complex effects on brain activity. It is absorbed from the lungs rapidly enough for each inhalation to have an almost immediate and separate

> Several years ago, I fell madly in love with an ex-smoker... a fanatic on the subject of cigarettes... I had always thought I'd be able to kick my addiction for someone I loved. That assumption turned out to be wrong. In the end, when forced to choose between love and cigarettes, I chose cigarettes.
>
> Quoted in A.Weil and W.Rosen, *From Chocolate to Morphine*, Haughton Mifflin Company, 1998

effect. Nicotine levels build up over smoking a cigarette and then rapidly decline until the next 'smoke'. Immediacy of impact is thought to contribute to the attraction of smoking, while the rapid decline permits frequent use.

One or two cigarettes increase pulse rate and blood pressure, reduce appetite, lower skin temperature and produce symptoms of stimulation and arousal. Smokers can effectively use smoking to alleviate stress and anxiety, but also to maintain performance in the face of fatigue or monotony. While regular smokers experience satisfaction on inhaling, first-time users often feel sick and dizzy.

LONG-TERM USE

Marked tolerance rapidly develops to the effects of nicotine. The more one smokes, the more likely one is to suffer from heart disease, blood clots, heart attacks, lung infections, strokes, bronchitis, bad circulation, lung cancer, cancer of the mouth and throat, and ulcers. Few will get all these effects, but everybody who smokes is more likely to suffer from each. As a result, tobacco contributes to at least 120,000 premature deaths in the UK every year: half of all teenage cigarette smokers will die 'before their time' if they continue smoking.

Lung cancer is the disease most closely associated with smoking. Risk of irreversible damage to the lungs increases with the number of cigarettes smoked per day, the number of years of smoking, and the earliness of the age at which one started. However, if no irreversible damage has yet occurred the lungs clear themselves once smoking has stopped and the ex-smoker can regain normal health and life expectancy. Since the 1950s, increased use of filter-tips and decreased average cigarette strength may have contributed to a reduction in lung cancer in Britain. However, recent evidence suggests that although 'low tar' or 'mild' cigarettes have lower tar levels, smokers tend to inhale deeper and more often, to the extent that any benefits are cancelled out.

The most striking aspect of cigarette use is the extent of dependence and regular use. People who begin to smoke tend to increase their consumption until they smoke regularly. If they stop, they may feel restless, irritable and depressed. More people are regular users of tobacco than any other drug.

Large tobacco corporations have been forced into admitting that tobacco is addictive – a fact they have apparently known for many years, but kept secret. Court cases have been heard and are being planned in pursuit of damages claims against the companies both in the UK and USA. Some of the tobacco companies have offered out of court, blanket compensation deals to protect themselves from further litigation.

It is now well established in the literature that the population is at risk from the effects of passive smoking, ranging from respiratory irritations, infections and asthma (especially children) through to cancer.

SPECIAL CASES

Women who smoke beyond the first months of pregnancy tend to give birth to smaller and less mature babies, which may give rise to difficulties after the birth. They also run a slightly increased risk of spontaneous abortion and increase the (still very small) risk of losing the baby around the time of birth. Women who smoke and take oral contraceptives are ten times more likely to suffer from diseases of the heart or circulatory system than women who do neither.

Solvents

Some organic – that is, carbon-based – compounds, produce effects similar to alcohol or anaesthetics when their vapours are inhaled. So long as the substance gives off vapour or is a gas at normal temperatures, products like these can be inhaled through the mouth or nose to achieve a drug-type effect, a practice commonly (although erroneously) referred to as 'glue sniffing'. Often sniffers use devices to heighten this effect by increasing the concentration of vapour and/or excluding air, for instance, by sniffing from inside a plastic bag placed over the head.

Solvent misuse has been known in Britain since at least 1962 and in America since the 1950s, but in the UK concern has built up only since the mid-1970s.

LEGAL STATUS

Under the Intoxicating Substances (Supply) Act 1985, it is an offence to supply or offer to supply solvents to persons aged under 18 if the supplier has reason to believe that they intend to misuse them. The Cigarette Lighter Refill (Safety) Regulations 1999, on the other hand, removes the onus of intention by making it an offence to sell butane refills to anyone under 18 years of age, regardless of whether the retailer is aware of its intended use. In Scotland, it is an offence to 'recklessly' sell solvents to children knowing they intend to inhale them. Other than this, selling, possessing or sniffing solvents is not restricted. Sniffers may be convicted for unruly, offensive or intoxicated behaviour, or because they resist police attempts to intervene. Someone driving under the influence of solvents may be convicted of driving while unfit.

Solvents have been ruled to be 'drugs' in the offence of being in charge of a vehicle while unfit through drink or drugs.

Solvent misusers have offended against a variety of laws and by-laws dealing with unruly, offensive, alarming or intoxicated behaviour, most commonly related to breach of the peace. No more need be involved than inhaling solvents in public, causing alarm to passers-by. However, breach of the peace is not a criminal offence and there is no 'criminal record'.

PRODUCTION AND SUPPLY

A number of solvents have applications in glues, paints, nail varnish removers, dry cleaning fluids and de-greasing compounds; others are used as propellant gases (in aerosols and fire extinguishers) or as fuels (petrol, cigarette lighter gas). Most of these solvents are available from a large number of retail outlets and can be found in nearly every household.

PREVALENCE

Overall, several recent British studies have found that between 7–10% of secondary school pupils have tried solvents, and that sniffing peaks around the third and fourth years of secondary schooling, whereby as many as 21% of 15–16-year-olds say they have tried solvents.

LICIT AND ILLICIT USE

Solvent misuse seems to become common in very localised areas, perhaps confined to an estate or a school, sometimes quickly disappearing. So in some places, at some times, a significant proportion of local adolescents (predominantly aged between 12 and 16) experiment with solvent sniffing, and a smaller proportion may continue for several months or longer after the vogue has passed among their peers. The government has published guidelines for retailers, advising that 'sniffable' products are stocked out of reach of children, and that sales staff refuse to sell these products to children whom they suspect may misuse them. Unfortunately, there are indications that putting adhesives out of the reach of young people has simply encouraged a switch to more dangerous solvents, such as butane lighter fuel.

PRICE

In comparison to a lot of substances, solvents come out particularly inexpensive, possibly one reason for their popularity with younger users. Butane gas can be purchased for around £1.50. Glues sell for the same or less, to be used by more than one user on more than one occasion.

Solvents

SHORT-TERM USE

Inhaled solvent vapours are absorbed through the lungs and rapidly reach the brain. Part of the effect is due to reduced oxygen intake. Generally, body functions like breathing and heart rate are depressed, and repeated or deep inhalation can result in an 'overdose' causing disorientation, loss of control and unconsciousness, from which in normal circumstances the sniffer quickly recovers with no lasting harm.

The experience of solvent inhalation is like being very drunk on alcohol. Feelings of dizziness, unreality and euphoria are common, but some experimenters just feel sick or drowsy. Lowering of inhibitions can result in unusually gregarious or emotional behaviour, depending partly on the circumstances. 'Pseudohallucinations' (the person knows they are unreal) commonly occur. Most sniffers enjoy and to some extent can control their experiences; a few become depressed or feel overwhelmed.

But unlike drinking alcohol, the effects come on quickly and disappear within 15 to 45 minutes if sniffing is stopped. Afterwards, the sniffer often feels drowsy and may sleep. Later, they may experience a mild 'hangover' (with symptoms such as headaches and poor concentration) for about a day.

On average about 100 young people die every year from solvent use; increasingly these deaths are happening as a direct result of the toxic effects of the substances on the body (especially butane lighter fuel), rather than indirectly. Such 'indirect' deaths would be through choking on vomit, accidents through being intoxicated, or suffocation through sniffing a solvent in a large plastic bag over the head.

LONG-TERM USE

Very long-term (e.g. ten years), heavy solvent misuse might result in moderate, lasting impairment of brain function, affecting especially the control of movement. Chronic misuse of aerosols and cleaning fluids has caused lasting kidney and liver damage, while repeatedly sniffing leaded petrol may result in lead poisoning.

Despite these possibilities, lasting damage attributable to solvent misuse seems extremely rare. In Britain, the evidence is limited to a few isolated cases, and surveys of groups of sniffers have not revealed any persistent medical consequences.

However, temporary impairment is more common. While someone is sniffing repeatedly, the 'hangover' effects of pallor, fatigue, forgetfulness and loss of concentration can become a recurring daily pattern affecting their performance and functioning, and there can be weight loss, depression, tremor and interference with liver and kidney function, but these will clear up once sniffing is discontinued.

Tolerance develops, such that perhaps after a year, a sniffer may have to inhale several times more than they started with in order to get high. Occasionally, withdrawal symptoms have been observed, but physical dependence is not a recognised problem. Psychological dependence on the effects of solvents develops in a minority of susceptible youngsters with underlying family or personality problems, and these will probably become 'lone-sniffers' as opposed to the usual pattern of sniffing in groups. Regarding the effects of sniffing on the foetus, there is some limited evidence in the literature that babies born to mothers who have regularly sniffed solvents containing Toluene during pregnancy, may be born with various abnormalities similar to foetal alcohol syndrome.

SPECIAL CASES

Those with heart complaints and low blood pressure are at particular risk if they inhale solvents, which can lead to heart failure or collapse.

Over-the-counter drugs (OTC)

There are some medicinal preparations (cold/flu relief and cough syrups) which can be bought over the counter from pharmacists without prescription. These contain mood-altering drugs with similar (although milder) effects to drugs such as heroin, amphetamine and benzodiazepines. Users may turn to these medicines when cash or supplies of their drug of choice are low.

OTC drugs can be roughly divided into three groups: those containing ingredients with an opiate-like effect; preparations with a stimulant effect; and those with a sedative action. Many preparations contain a cocktail of ingredients which highlights some of the problems in deciding precisely why a particular medicine has become popular with drug users – it could be the sedative, or the stimulant effect or that the combination of drugs in a compound medicine work together to provide a certain kind of euphoric effect. Only those medicines most commonly reported as being misused are mentioned here in this very brief review.

Medicines containing opioids

These preparations are usually cough medicines or painkillers. The opioids suppress the cough reflex or exert an analgesic effect. Many contain codeine, an opiate that has milder yet similar analgesic properties to morphine. In fact, after ingestion 10% of the drug is converted by the body to morphine.

Cough medications containing codeine usually come in syrup formulation, making injection unlikely. However, there have been reports of users separating codeine from codeine-containing tablets (e.g. co-codaprin), using a coffee percolator. One danger from this practice is that nearly 75% of the aspirin in these tablets remains after filtration. Aspirin poisoning is possible if too much of the filtered remains are injected at any one time. One tablet cuts out this process, however. Nurofen Plus, because it is a bi-layer tablet, that is, it is made up of a white layer of ibuprofen and another of codeine, requires little other effort than splitting the tablet in half and removing the ibuprofen.

Medicines with a stimulant effect

These include cough syrups, cold remedies and nasal decongestants where a (pseudo)stimulant such as ephedrine or oxymetazoline is included to dry up a runny nose (pseudo because it is not a central nervous stimulant as such, but encourages the body to release a type of adrenaline – a chemical which increases heart rate and alertness). The stimulant-type action of these preparations was particularly well known in the 1990s when brands such as Vicks Sinex and Sudafed were used by some clubbers to supposedly enhance the effect of ecstasy and amphetamine.

Medicines containing antihistamine

Many OTC cough and cold products contain antihistamines like diphenhydramine (Nytol) and promethazine (Phenergan and Sominex). Nytol has been identified from surveys of pharmacists as one of the medicines most likely to be misused after the opiate-based products. If taken correctly, antihistamines are safe. However, if taken in large doses and if the sedative effect can be overcome, they can exert a psychoactive effect. Dangers arise when the sedative action of these drugs is increased significantly by the consumption of alcohol.

The concern for potential for misuse is highlighted by the removal in the 1980s of the antihistamine medication Sleepia, which contained diphenhydramine. Its removal followed concerns, mainly in Glasgow, that the gel-filled capsules were proving popular among injecting drug users. It was feared users were buying the drug to complement or replace methadone prescriptions and even street heroin – with the inherent risk of overdose and other risks associated with injecting.

Diphenhydramine is still available from chemists as Nytol, Dreemon and Panadol Night. Though the latter, because it also contains 500mg of paracetamol, is less prone to misuse. Users are aware of the dangers too much paracetamol can cause the liver and so tend to avoid compound analgesics.

Over-the-counter drugs

SUPPLY AND PREVALENCE

Since the government removed certain branded drugs from NHS Prescription Only status (POM) and made them pharmacy (P) or OTC medicines, self-medication has helped reduce costs to the NHS. It may also have led to an increase in misuse of these drugs. In order for medicines to achieve OTC status, they must satisfy strict criteria. These include having low toxicity, having a wide therapeutic index, low overdose threshold, and minimal clinical interaction with other medicines. Despite these regulations, and a common perception that these drugs are not so strong as prescription only drugs, they can contain higher doses of the active ingredients, such as antihistamines, than those prescribed by GPs.

Not much is known about who typically misuses these drugs. OverCount, based in Dumfries, specialising in OTC misuse, deal with a lot of people, mainly women, in the 25 to 35-years-age group. Users vary greatly, however, from young experimenters to polydrug users supplementing their normal drug consumption. No prevalence figures exist either, though OverCount estimate their annual client base could reach 10,000 clients a year. The main areas of OTC misuse are thought to concentrate in London and the South-East, central Scotland, Aberdeen and the Grampians. Misusers typically have more than one source for their supply, usually in an attempt to avoid alerting pharmacy staff to their problem. It is not unknown for an individual to spend a day visiting many pharmacists, possibly miles apart, to purchase a single week's consumption.

Other drugs

Many drugs such as cannabis, ecstasy and heroin are constants on the illicit drug scene. Other drugs like barbiturates were once very common, but are now rarely seen on the streets. Drug users are always looking for new drugs to try. These might be new variants on existing illegal drugs such as crack (smokeable cocaine) or Ice (smokeable methamphetamine). They might also be drugs that fall outside the controlled drug laws, such as ketamine, or they may be Prescription Only Medicines.

Below is some general information about drugs which have a lower profile on the UK drug scene.

GHB

GHB, or 'GBH' as it has been dubbed on the street and in the press, is gammahydroxybutyrate or sodium oxybate – an anaesthetic with primarily sedative rather than painkilling properties. GHB is also present in the body in small amounts and in certain ripe fruits such as guava.

GHB is often sold as liquid ecstasy because of its relaxant and euphoric effects, similar to that of alcohol. Recently, however, it has been linked to date rape, when the drug is mixed with alcohol, rendering the recipient incapable.

Legal status

GHB is controlled under the Misuse of Drugs Act as a Class C drug.

Production and supply

GHB is a colourless, odourless liquid with a slightly salty taste, which is sold in small bottles. These bottles might have a warning label advising against drinking alcohol at the same time as taking the contents. It has also been seen in powder and capsule form. One UK company that deals in 'smart drugs' has GHB in its catalogue, in the form of capsules imported from the USA. The catalogue promotes GHB as a cure for insomnia, tagging it 'Nature's Quaalude'. Quaaludes are the US equivalent of the once popular sedative known in the UK as Mandrax (methaqualone). GHB is a banned substance in America, but a related substance GBL (Gamma Buty Lactone) is not. As a result, GBL is being widely used in America. Once ingested, the body converts GBL into GHB.

GHB is easily made using certain solvents and caustic soda (a potentially risky procedure because of the caustic soda). The bottles mentioned above appear to contain about 40ml of liquid. The drug can be bought at sex and head shops, and at some clubs and dance events.

Prevalence

None of the large UK surveys included GHB in their enquiries, so there is no way of estimating the extent of GHB use in the UK. Its use appears to be restricted to dance events as well as used experimentally by young people, but it is not thought to be currently widespread.

Other drugs

Licit and illicit drug use

GHB was developed in the USA, as a premedication to promote sleep before surgery. Recreationally, GHB seems to have found favour with two groups of users. Because it promotes what is known as 'slow wave sleep', during which growth hormone is secreted, GHB has been used by bodybuilders. The other group are those on the dance and club scene both here and in the States. In Britain its use has particularly been noted in gay clubs.

One street name for GHB is 'liquid ecstasy'. However, people are taking the drug for its euphoric and sedative effects rather than as a stimulant which aids dancing – an alternative to getting drunk on alcohol rather than a dance/partying drug. The drug is mainly taken by mouth, although there is at least one report of users injecting it.

Doses are 'measured' out in various ad hoc ways which result in different amounts of the drug being consumed. Some consider a bottle contains roughly three doses – about a 15ml tablespoon each. Elsewhere, it has been written that the customary dose is 5ml – a teaspoon. Doses are also measured out as capfuls, an indeterminate quantity in roughly the same range.

Adding to the confusion is the fact that there is no telling how concentrated the liquid is, or whether it is actually GHB, and not GBL. GBL is known to have a stronger ability to sedate someone, and so is more effective in date rape. Even if it is GHB, a given bottle could contain around three grams of the drug, in theory quite a mild dose, or up to 20 grams, a very high dose. Where people have simply swallowed the whole bottle, dosages at anything like this level would help explain some of the more extreme reactions listed below.

Price

Prices have been reported at around £5 for a capful of liquid and £10–£15 a bottle. The mail order price, quoted by the smart drug company mentioned above, is around £16 for 20 capsules each containing 250mg.

Short-term use

The effects of GHB are noticeable between ten minutes and an hour after taking the drug and have been reported as lasting a day or longer. Like alcohol, in small doses GHB will break down social inhibitions and increase libido. Some users have likened the effect to ecstasy, others (who remember it) to methaqualone. As the dosage increases, euphoria gives way to powerful sedative effects and there have been reports of nausea, vomiting, stiffening of muscles, disorientation, convulsions, coma and respiratory collapse.

Although symptoms such as coma can be very frightening for those who witness them, so far, people who have been hospitalised because of these symptoms have made a rapid and full recovery.

The drug is also being increasingly linked to date rape, in the same way as Rohypnol is used to sedate a victim – rendering them incapable. GHB is both odourless and tasteless and has its effects enhanced by alcohol, making it an easy drug to add to alcohol without detection. Two cases of GHB used for this purpose have been confirmed. A report by the Metropolitan Police acknowledges the existence of this problem, making several recommendations for research, better handling of complainants, and advice on preparing evidence for court.

Mixing with other drugs

There have been a number of disturbing reports of fatal mixes of GHB and alcohol. Clearly, any dangers will be enhanced from mixing the drug with other sedative drugs and will also be determined by the weight and gender of the person, their general health and so on.

Long-term Use

Like any drug with sedative effects, there is the potential for physical and psychological dependence; one case of the former is cited in the literature. Other possible long-term consequences are unknown.

KETAMINE

Ketamine is a very complex drug, an anaesthetic with analgesic, stimulant and psychedelic properties, chemically related to phencyclidine (PCP, angel dust). Like PCP, ketamine is a 'dissociative' anaesthetic: patients feel detached and remote from their immediate environment.

Ketamine also induces a cataleptic state of muscle rigidity: a patient placed in one position cannot subsequently move until the effect has worn off. Together, these properties made ketamine very useful in emergency surgery – it was used widely during the Vietnam War.

The key to the ketamine experience in sub-anaesthetic doses is dissociation: users say that under its influence, they assume a different point of view, outside of body and self. Because of this, some psychotherapists have experimented with ketamine to test its potential as a psychotherapeutic tool.

Legal status

Ketamine is not controlled under the Misuse of Drugs Act and possession is not a criminal offence, although this is currently under review. It is, however, a Prescription Only Medicine under the Medicines Act, meaning unauthorised supply is illegal.

Production and supply

It is not known whether illicit supplies have been illicitly manufactured from scratch or reformulated from licit sources such as hospitals or vets. However, it is possible that, currently, street ketamine derives from licit sources, where diverted liquid is heated to evaporate the water, leaving ketamine crystals. The drug is retailed like other illicit drugs such as ecstasy, often replacing that drug when not available.

Ketamine comes in a variety of forms ranging from its liquid pharmaceutical state, for injecting, through to pills to be taken orally. Powders are sniffed up the nose or sometimes smoked.

Prevalence

Reports of ketamine's recreational use have been geographically widespread from southern England to Scotland. It appears to be widely used on the dance scene; one small study estimated that nearly 25% of those who took drugs at dances and clubs had tried ketamine.

Licit and illicit use

Ketamine first appeared as a street drug in America during the early 1970s in a variety of forms ranging from its liquid pharmaceutical state, for injecting, through to pills to be taken orally, powders intended to be sniffed up the nose, and a formulation for smoking. Ketamine appears to have emerged from the same dance culture which has embraced ecstasy.

The 'normal' dose for sniffing ketamine is about 60–100mg. Used intravenously or intramuscularly, a sub-anaesthetic dose would be around 1–2mg per kg of body weight.

Price

Prices range from £10–£20 per gram, though this may not always be pure ketamine.

Short-term use

Ketamine takes effect over varying time periods, depending on the route of administration (from 30 seconds for intravenous injection to 20 minutes taken orally), and the effects can last up to three hours.

Reported physical effects include an initial cocaine-like rush, vomiting and nausea, slurring of speech and vision, numbness and ataxia (irregular muscle coordination). Many users report a temporary paralysis and a feeling of being out of the body.

Aside from the risks from injecting common to all drugs, it is ketamine's anaesthetic properties which pose the main physical dangers. Under its influence, users are less likely to feel pain and, combined with the fact that some might not realise they are hallucinating (because they believe what is happening is real), there is the potential for serious injury.

Other drugs

As with any anaesthetic, eating or drinking in the hours prior to use could cause vomiting; because of the risks of choking, this could be particularly dangerous if too much is taken and the user falls unconscious. If the dose exceeds the standard surgical dose, then there is the risk of respiratory collapse or heart failure. Some deaths have been reported.

Users report that although ketamine's psychological effects come on and recede faster than with LSD, these effects are similar – including hallucinations, synaesthesia ('seeing' sounds and 'hearing' colours), euphoria, de-personalisation and confusion, plus the powerful dissociative or out-of-body (flying or floating) sensations, which appear specific to ketamine. Different from the LSD experience, however, are the reported feelings of aggression and stimulation.

What are the long-term effects?

Not only is ketamine the only hallucinogen users inject, but it may be the only one that is actually psychologically addictive – primarily because of the powerful detachment and heightened visual and potentially spiritual experiences which occur. With repeated use, tolerance develops quickly.

In general, the literature on the consequences of long-term ketamine use is sparse, and the following observations are invariably based on single case studies. Flashbacks (short-lived recurrences of the drug experience) similar to that experienced by some LSD users are possible. One clinical report suggests there may be memory, attention and vision impairment from long-term use, which in this case did not return to normal once use was reduced.

Frequent and prolonged use of ketamine could cause the same problems as phencyclidine, including psychological dependence, psychosis and gradual loss of contact with the real world.

KHAT

Catha edulis, commonly known as *qat* or *qaadka* in Somalia, or *chat* in Ethiopia, but now referred to consistently in the literature as khat, is a green leafy plant chewed across northern Africa and in Arabia. Khat contains two known pharmacologically active substances, cathinone (aminopropiophenone) and cathine (norpseudoephedrine).

Cathinone is the main active ingredient. Its concentration in the fresh leaves ranges from 0.3 to 2.1%, depending on the origin and variety of the plant. Cathine concentrations range from 0.7 to 2.7%. The active ingredients start to deteriorate two days after the plant has been harvested, meaning it must be consumed fresh.

Legal status

The khat plant itself is not controlled under the Misuse of Drugs Act, but the active ingredients, cathinone and cathine, are Class C drugs. Cathinone may not be lawfully possessed or supplied except under a licence for research, though cathine may be prescribed. The legal status of khat is currently under review.

Production and supply

The plant is cultivated throughout eastern Africa and the Arabian peninsula at altitudes of 1,500–2,000 metres. There are several varieties of the plant, but two are generally available: Miraa chiefly from Kenya and the Harari from Ethiopia. It is imported either as fresh leaves or sometimes as twigs into the UK. The plant can be purchased at some specialist health food shops, markets and in a number of head shops. Traditional users of the drug choose to eat only fresh leaves as the dried plant contains no (or very little) active chemicals.

Prevalence

Somali refugees seeking asylum in Britain because of the civil war in their country are the main group associated with khat in the British press. In the UK, it is also used to some extent by groups from Ethiopia and the Arabian peninsula. There is little evidence to suggest khat is being used in the UK except in these communities.

Licit and illicit use

Medical use of khat dates back to antiquity, when Alexander the Great used it to treat his soldiers for an unknown 'epidemic disease'. In the Harar region of Ethiopia, khat is widely believed to effect 501 different kinds of cures; these equal the numerical value of its Arabic name: ga-a-t (400+100+1).

Khat has been chewed or drunk in the Muslim cultures of Somalia and Yemen for centuries, where it has been considered a rival to coffee. It was mentioned in an Arab manuscript in 1333. In modern times, so important is khat as a commodity that its daily export to Aden lay behind the founding of Ethiopian Airlines.

Price

Prices vary, but a small bundle of leaves weighing two to three ounces will cost roughly £4.

Short-term use

Khat is predominantly stimulant in effect. A typical khat chewing session is said to be the equivalent of ingesting a moderate 5mg dose of amphetamine sulphate. Following mild euphoria and talkativeness, users have often reported calming effects.

Because it is chewed, khat affects the oral cavity and the digestive tract. Inflammation of the mouth and other parts of the oral cavity, with secondary infections, is common in khat users.

Long-term use

There is evidence that excessive use of khat can lead to other health problems, such as heart disease and loss of sex drive in men. Of particular concern is the risk of oral cancer, reportedly prevalent among khat chewers in Yemen. Prolonged and excessive use can bring on psychological problems such as depression, anxiety and irritation, sometimes leading to psychosis. It is becoming apparent (especially in London) that khat use is often overlooked by mental health workers.

Many Somalis (and people from other khat using cultures) do not acknowledge the problems that have been identified with khat. This may be related to the fact that in their home countries most users chew on a social or moderate basis. In the UK, some have escalated their consumption as a reaction to their changed circumstances and the frustrations of life as a refugee.

Other drugs

2CB

An hallucinogen related to ecstasy, also known as Nexus or Brom, or by chemists as 4-Bromo-2,5-Dimethoxyphenethylamine. A relative newcomer to the UK illicit market, it made its emergence on the dance scene as an alternative and a complementary drug to ecstasy. The drug is sold either as a white powder or as small pills.

Legal status

2CB is categorised as belonging to the ecstasy family of drugs, and is therefore a Class A drug. It is illegal to produce, supply or possess the drug in any form. No doctor can prescribe it and anybody wanting to use it for research purposes has to obtain a licence from the Home Office.

Production and supply

2CB was developed by Alexander Shulgin, an American chemist responsible for over 200 psychoactive compounds, nearly all of which he has administered to himself. Most of what we know in the literature is based on his accounts.

The drug is manufactured in illegal laboratories at home and abroad. Production sources as far away as India and Thailand have been reported, with routes passing through Turkey and the Balkans on the drug's way to Western Europe.

Prevalence

At the moment there are no figures for levels of use in the UK. Clubbers and ravers are more likely to come across the drug than other user groups.

Licit and illicit use

Seen as a complementary drug to ecstasy, 2CB was sold on the premise that if taken at the peak of ecstasy intoxication, heightened stimulation would ensue, lengthening the period of the high. Its use therefore is closely identified with ecstasy and the dance scene, although it too can be taken on its own. The drug is normally swallowed, but it can also be snorted or smoked.

Price

As a relatively uncommon drug, prices vary. For a standard dose of 20mg of 2CB, prices start at £5, going up to £25 for stronger doses of around 40mg.

Short-term use

2CB is highly dosage sensitive. In its pure state, the drug is active at 15–40 mg, depending on one's body size and sensitivity. At lower doses, the drug is described as an energetic experience similar to ecstasy. At higher doses, the experience is similar to that of LSD and ecstasy. People have reported heightened visual imagery, acute awareness of their bodies and increased sensitivity to smells, tastes and sexual stimulation. Effects seem to last from two to four hours, longer if taken on top of ecstasy.

Mixing with other drugs

Because the drug is relatively new and not widespread, little is known both anecdotally and clinically about the drug's effects when taken with other drugs. When taken together with ecstasy, the drug is said to intensify feelings of exhilaration, extending the length of intoxication. However, feelings of nausea and anxiety are also likely to intensify. As with ecstasy and amphetamine, this drug should not be taken with MAOI anti-depressants. [See Cocaine and crack – **Mixing with other drugs** for more details]

Long-term use

There are no selective studies into the effects of 2CB use. However, experiences from other drugs, such as ecstasy and LSD, suggest that regular use can leave the user feeling fatigued, disorientated, and anxious. Users may also experience depression, and vulnerable individuals may experience psychotic syndromes, visual illusions, panic attacks and depersonalisation.

Users may also experience feelings of extreme confusion and distress, even to the extent of fearing they will never come back from the trip. Tolerance is rapid, and very large amounts are needed if effects are to be repeated within a short space of time.

LEGAL HIGHS

Herbal ecstasy

Herbal ecstasy has until recently been sold freely at raves, clubs, concerts and festivals. It contains various herbs and extracts that are claimed to be hallucinogenic and/or stimulant. Packaging and vendors claim that it is a natural and safe substitute for ecstasy. However, it often has side-effects similar to many synthetic drugs.

Ephedrine and Ma-Huang

Ephedrine is an extract of the Chinese herb Ma-Huang which has been reported to have stimulant effects such as shivers up and down the spine, sensitive skin and muscles, and feelings of exhilaration. In China, the herb Ma-Huang is sold as a medicine and as an aphrodisiac. Here it is sold as Cloud 9, Nirvana Plus, and other herbal highs said to mimic ecstasy. Higher doses can be quite unpleasant, possibly causing muscle spasms and even heart attack.

Yohimbe

Said to be an aphrodisiac and sold as an hallucinogenic with stimulant effects (also spelled yohimbine). It is marketed as Yohimbix8 or as an additive to other herbal highs. The drug is derived from the yohimbe tree roots. As with ephedrine higher doses can be quite unpleasant, possibly causing muscle spasms and even heart attack.

Packaging often states that these drugs, because they are natural and herbal, are safe or non-addictive. Any drug which has a psychological effect can prove difficult to stop if used regularly. Proper controlled research on these drugs is sparse, and therefore side-effects and possible dangers when taken with other drugs, and even foods, are not fully known.

Salvia

Salvia is derived from the American plant Salvia divinorum, a member of the mint family. It is used in shamanic rituals by the Mazatecs and other groups in Meso-America. Salvia is marketed in the UK as herbal ecstasy, as for example, Eclipse, or a legal hallucinogen. It is sold as a herbal remedy in health food shops and chemists under its botanical name. Its effects are more hallucinatory than the other legal highs and it has some stimulant properties. The drug is swallowed as a capsule or smoked in its dried leaf form (albeit in large quantities).

Legal status

Herbal highs are not controlled under the Misuse of Drugs Act, so possession is not an offence, as long as it is for personal use. The Home Office has expressed concern at the free sale of these drugs, which has led recently to the Medicines Control Agency treating them as medicines, so unauthorised manufacture and distribution could be an offence under the Medicines Act. However, this law does allow the drug to be legally imported for personal use only. As with poppers, enforcement is difficult in practice, and many unauthorised outlets avoid prosecution. To add to confusion, related compounds such as pseudoephedrine, found in over-the-counter preparations such as Nurofen cold and flu remedies and some decongestants, do not so far come under the Medicines Act, neither do Ma-Huang and yohimbe when sold as a herbs.

Production and supply

Imported as a spice in its raw form, yohimbe is grown in Asia; ephedrine comes from China, Japan and North America; and salvia from South America, mainly Mexico.

Ephedrine (and pseudoephedrine) is also produced by a number of pharmaceutical companies, as an additive in cough and cold remedies such as nasal decongestants. Both spices can be purchased from specialist spice and herbal shops. The drugs are also marketed in the UK as a herbal and legal alternative to ecstasy and as aphrodisiacs. The tablets can be purchased from sex and head shops, at dance events and festivals, and by mail order – the USA is a main source of imported herbal ecstasy pills.

Prevalence

As yet there are no statistics on the level of use in the UK.

Other drugs

Licit and illicit use

Ephedrine has been used by the Chinese since ancient times as a decongestant and cold remedy. Native Americans have traditionally infused the drug as a cure for syphilis, a brew apparently popular with early Mormons.

Ephedrine and pseudoephedrine are in general used as decongestants in tablet form, together with paracetamol or ibuprofen as a nasal spray. Their vasoconstricting properties make them useful for raising blood pressure during certain spinal operations. Marketed as legal and herbal highs, the drugs are used in similar ways to ecstasy at dance events and festivals.

Salvia imported in its raw form is sold in half-ounce bags or smaller, and sold at dance events or festivals. In capsule form, it is sold in head shops or through mail order.

Price

Packets containing four to six tablets or capsules retail for between £8 and £15 each.

Short-term use

Within approximately 45 minutes of being eaten, yohimbe raises blood pressure and increases heart rate. The drug has alleged aphrodisiac properties, increasing sensuality and sexual desire. The hallucinations are said to be quite strong and the effects on the body similar to that of ecstasy.

Ephedrine has effects similar to ecstasy also, although physical sensations are more pronounced. Side-effects include racing heart, dry throat, possible anxiety, tremor, and cold feet and hands. Salvia must be smoked in large quantities, usually two or three large pipefuls, and held in the lungs for up to 45 seconds. A trip lasts up to 45 minutes. The effects are said to similar to LSD, although more introspective with a slight stimulatory effect. The effects when swallowed are less profound and longer lasting.

Mixing with other drugs

Concern has been raised that ephedrine, and in particular yohimbe, when taken with some drugs and a number of amine-specific foods, can prove toxic. Cases of individuals collapsing after taking yohimbe and foods such as chocolate, cheese, sherry, pineapple, bananas, and other foods containing tryptophans, have been reported. Combinations with LSD, MDA and MDMA are also not without serious risk. MAOI drugs may also contribute to high blood pressure.

Long term use

The long-term effects of yohimbe, salvia or ephedrine use are not well documented. Regular use can lead to problems associated with hypertension such as dizziness, glaucoma and heart disease. As with most stimulants, repeated use can result in users feeling fatigued, possibly anxious and paranoid, leading to psychotic episodes.

Special cases

According to medics, these drugs should not be used by people with heart disease, diabetes, hypertension or kidney disease. These drugs are particularly dangerous if taken in combination with MAOI anti-depressants, and possibly some foods such as mature cheese and red wine – yohimbe is regarded as an inhibitor of MAOI itself. [*See* Cocaine and crack – **Mixing with other drugs** for more details]

Drug group

Principal drugs

Terms in capitals are for a class of drugs and are followed (in lower case) by examples of that class.

Scientific names

For plant drugs (cannabis, mushrooms, tobacco) the botanical name of the plant is followed in brackets by the active chemical ingredient. In other cases the generic or non-proprietary name of the drug is given.

Trade, slang and other names

Slang terms are in quotes. Common trade or proprietary names are given for drugs manufactured for medical use. General names for products containing that drug are given for drugs (alcohol, solvents, tobacco, caffeine) available in non-medical products.

tables

Legal status

Prescription Only Medicine
Available only on prescription under the Medicines Act.

Controlled drug
Controlled under the Misuse of Drugs Act. Illegal to possess without a prescription or other authority unless otherwise indicated.

Recommended medical uses

As recommended in official UK prescribing guides or customary medical use.

Effects

Covers immediate psychological and physical effects and the risks of physical dependence. Does not cover potential consequences of long-term use.

Drugs that depress the nervous system

Drug group	Principal drugs		Legal status
	Scientific names	*Trade, slang & other names*	
ALCOHOLIC BEVERAGES	ethyl alcohol or ethanol	'BOOZE' etc, beers, wines, spirits, liqueurs	Can be bought by adults (18+) and drunk outside a pub/bar by children (5+). Need license to sell.
BENZODIAZEPINES, MINOR TRANQUILLISERS, 'TRANX'	MINOR TRANQUILLISERS diazepam	'Tranx' Valium, Diazemuls, Tensium, Valclair, Stesolid, Rimapam	Prescription Only Medicines. Controlled drugs. Illegal to possess without a prescription.
	alprazolam	Xanax	
	clorazepate dipotassium	Tranxene	
	midazolam	Midazolam, Hypnovel	
	chlordiazepoxide	Librium, Tropium	
	orazepam	Ativan	
	oxazepam	Oxazepam	
	nitrazepam	Mogadon, Remnos, Somnite	
	flurazepam	Dalmane	
	flunitrazepam	Rohypnol	
	temazepam	Temazepam, 'Tems', 'Eggs', 'Jellies'	
	oprazolam	Dormonoct	
	ormetazepam	Lormetazepam	
SOLVENTS AND GASES	toluene	Glue	In the UK is illegal to sell any solvent knowingly for inhalation, except for butane lighter fuels that cannot be sold to under 18-year-olds. In Scotland misusers may be taken into care.
	acetone	Glue	
	butane	Lighter fuel	
	fluorocarbons	Aerosols	
	trichloroethylene	Cleaning fluid	
	trichloroethane	Cleaning fluid	
GHB	gammahydroxybutyrate	GBH liquid ecstasy	Controlled drug.

Drug group tables

Recommended medical uses	Methods of administration	Prevalence and availability	Effects
None.	Swallowed as a beverage.	Available through over 170,000 licensed premises. Over 9 in 10 adults drink to some extent.	Depress the nervous system, relieve tension and anxiety, promote relaxation, impair the efficiency of mental and physical functioning, and decrease self-control. In higher doses there can be 'drunken' behaviour, drowsiness, stupor, sleep/unconsciousness. With the exception of minor tranquillisers, these effects may be associated with positive feelings of pleasure. Tolerance develops with frequently repeated doses. In high doses there can be strong physical dependence to alcohol or hypnosedatives, less strong to minor tranquillisers, not at all to solvents or gases. Depressant effects may be dangerously augmented if more than one depressant drug is taken at a time, or if depressant drugs are taken with opiate-type drugs.
Relieve anxiety. Promote sleep in insomnia.	Swallowed as pills or capsules.	Most commonly prescribed drugs in Britain. Also available on the illicit market.	
None.	Vapours or gases inhaled through nose/mouth.	Widely available in shops, homes and places of work. Some 5–10% of secondary school pupils may have tried them.	
None.	Swallowed as liquid, powder or capsule.	Available in sex shops and head shops, sometimes in clubs or at festivals.	Similar to alcohol in small doses. Larger doses induce feelings of sedation, euphoria, reducing inhibitions. May also cause nausea, stiffening of the limbs and disorientation. Effects may last up to 24 hours. May cause problems if taken with other depressants such as alcohol.

Drugs that reduce pain

Drug group	Principal drugs		Legal status
	Scientific names	*Trade, slang & other names*	
OPIATES, OPIOIDS, NARCOTIC ANALGESICS	diacetylmorphine, diamorphine, or heroin	'Junk', 'skag', 'H', 'smack', Diamorphine, Diconal, 'dike'	Prescription Only Medicines, except in the form of some very dilute mixtures(*) available without prescription from pharmacies. Controlled drugs, but(*) legal to possess without a prescription.
	dipipanone	Physeptone, 'amps'	
	methadone	(injectable), 'linctus' (oral), Methex, Metharose, Methadose, 'mixture' (oral)	
	hydromorphone	Palladone	
	buprenorphine	Temgesic	
	pethidine	Pamergan, Pethidine	
	dextromoramide	Palfium	
	dextropropoxyphene	Doloxene	
	pentazocine	Fortral	
	meptazinol	Meptid	
	nalbuphine	Nubain	
	papaveretum	Papaveretum, Hyoscine Injection	
	tramadol	Tramadol, Tramake, Zamadol, Zydol, Dromadol	
	fentanyl	Durogesic, Sublimaze	
	alfenatil	Rapifen	
	opium	Opium	
	morphine	Cyclimorph, Oramorph, Sevredol, kaolin & morphine*	
	codeine	Codeine phosphate, Kapake, Co-codarprin*, Co-Codamol*, Tylex, Kaodine*, Benylin with Codeine*, Galcodine*, Nurofen Plus*, Codafen*	
	dihydrocodeine	DF118, DHC Continus, Remedeine, Co-dydramol	
	diphenoxylate	Lomotil	
	alfentanil	Rapifen	
	oxycodone	Oxynorm, Oxycontin	

Drug group tables

Recommended medical uses	Methods of administration	Prevalence and availability	Effects
Pain relief, cough suppression, anti-diarrhoea agents. Treatment of opiate dependence (methadone).	Heroin can be smoked, sniffed or injected. Most other opiate preparations can be injected or swallowed.	Illicitly produced and imported heroin is the most widely misused of this class of drugs. In many areas heroin is commonly available on the illicit market. Other opiates available from doctors or by theft. Perhaps 250,000 regular users.	Reduce sensitivity to and emotional reaction to pain, discomfort and anxiety. Feelings of warmth, contentment. Relatively little interference with mental or physical functioning. Higher doses, sedation, stupor, sleep/unconsciousness. Tolerance and physical dependence with frequently repeated doses. Depressant effects may be dangerously magnified if more than one opiate is taken at a time, or if opiates are taken with other depressant drugs.

Drugs that stimulate the nervous system

Drug group	Principal drugs		Legal status
	Scientific names	*Trade, slang & other names*	
AMPHETAMINES and amphetamine-like drugs	AMPHETAMINES amphetamine sulphate dexamphetamine (combination of the above) methamphetamine	'Uppers', 'speed' 'sulphate', 'sulph', 'whizz' Dexedrine 'Ice'	Prescription Only Medicines. Controlled drugs.
	AMPHETAMINE-LIKE DRUGS methylphenidate phentermine modafinil sibutramine	 Equasym, Ritalin Ionamin Provigil Reductil	
COCAINE	cocaine hydrochloride	'coke', 'snow'	Prescription Only Medicines. Controlled drugs.
	cocaine freebase	'crack', 'freebase', 'base', 'rock', 'wash', 'stone'	
CAFFEINE	caffeine	Coffee Tea Cocoa Soft drinks Chocolate Analgesic pills	Unrestricted.
TOBACCO	nicotiana tabacum nicotiana rustica nicotiana persica	Tobacco Cigarettes Snuff	Illegal to sell to children under 16. Otherwise unrestricted.
ANABOLIC STEROIDS	anabolic steroids	Nadrolone/Deca-durabolin Stanozolol/Stromba Dianabol Durabolin	Prescription Only Medicines. Class C under the Misuse of Drugs Act.
ALKYL NITRITES	Amyl nitrite Butyl nitrite Isobutyl nitrite	'Poppers' 'rush' 'Locker room' 'Hard core'	Pharmacy medicine.

Drug group tables

Recommended medical uses	Methods of administration	Prevalence and availability	Effects
Treatment of narcolepsy and hyperkinesia. Short-term treatment of obesity.	Amphetamine sulphate powder sniffed up the nose and injected. Some pills and capsules by mouth. Methamphetamine smoked as 'Ice'.	Illicitly manufactured amphetamine sulphate commonly available on the illicit market, plus some pills and capsules produced for medical use. Some methamphetamine available. After cannabis, probably the most widely misused controlled drug.	Except for steroids and nitrites, drugs that stimulate the nervous system increase alertness, diminish fatigue, delay sleep, increase ability to maintain vigilance or perform physical tasks over a long period, and elevate mood. Excepting tobacco, high doses can cause nervousness, anxiety and (with the exception
Rarely prescribed. Local anaesthetic.	Cocaine hydrochloride powder sniffed up the nose, sometimes injected. Cocaine freebase smoked.	Illicitly manufactured and imported hydrochloride powder available on the illicit market, but more expensive than other stimulants.	of tobacco and caffeine) temporary paranoid psychosis. Withdrawal effects include hunger and fatigue. Although unpleasant, these effects
None.	Swallowed as a beverage, in confectionery or in pills.	Freely available in beverages and foodstuffs taken regularly by the great majority of people in Britain.	are practically never of the kind that might require medical assistance.
None.	Smoked. Snuff is sniffed up the nose.	Widely available in shops. 38% of UK adults smoke.	
Persistent anaemia. Protein build-up.	Swallowed as pills or injected.	Available in gymnasia, health clubs etc.	Potential for increasing aggression and sex drive in men and women; possible liver and heart damage; non-reversible 'virilising' effects in women (body hair; deep voice); growth stunting in adolescents; psychological dependence.
None.	Vapours inhaled through the mouth.	Available in sex shops, clubs, bars etc.	With nitrites 'rushing' sensation as blood vessels dilate; enhanced sexual pleasure; possible headaches, vomiting and dermatitis. Excessive use of nitrites could bring on methaemoglobinemia (severe vomiting, shock and unconsciousness) which has caused fatalities. Tolerance develops, but no reports of withdrawal or dependence.

Drugs that stimulate the nervous system continued

Drug group	Principal drugs		Legal status
	Scientific names	*Trade, slang & other names*	
HALLUCINOGENIC AMPHETAMINES	methylenedioxyamphetamine MDA MDMA MDEA 2CB (nexus) 4-MTA 2CI	'ecstasy' 'E' plus many names derived from shape and colour of drugs	Controlled drugs; not available for medical use.
KHAT	Catha edulis, cathinone (extract)	Kat, Khat, Qat, Quaadka	Khat plant itself is not controlled under the Misuse of Drugs Act, but the active ingredients, cathinone and cathine, are a controlled substance.
LEGAL HIGHS	ephedrine yohimbine salvia divinorum	Ephedrine Ma-Huang, Nirvana Plus, Cloud 9, nasal drops Yohimbine, Yohimbe, Yohimbix8 sage, Eclipse	Ma-Huang and salvia can be sold as a herb, however legal high preparations such as ephedrine pills and Eclipse are classified as pharmacy medicines.

Drug group tables

Recommended medical uses	Methods of administration	Prevalence and availability	Effects
None.	Swallowed as tablets or capsules.	Illicitly manufactured and generally available on the illicit market.	With ecstasy feelings of empathy with others at low doses; more amphetamine-like restlessness and anxiety at higher doses. Some of these drugs such as 2CB in sufficient doses elicit mild hallucinations, or visual distortions, which can last up to 8 hours.
None.	Normally fresh leaves are chewed slowly to release active incredients.	The plant is used primarily by some groups with a cultural history of use, such as refugees from Yemen, Ethiopia and Kenya. There is no evidence of considerable use outside of these groups.	The plant has to be chewed, often for hours to elicit mild to strong stimulant effects similar to amphetamine. Stimulation is said to give way to feelings of euphoria. As with most stimulants, regular use can cause anxiety, paranoia, and psychosis.
Ephedrine is used as a nasal decongestant. Yohimbe and salvia have no medical use. Ma-Huang is used a herbal remedy by for example oriental herbalists.	All are usually swallowed as herbs, pills or capsules. Salvia is also smoked.	These drugs are not widely available, being sold by specialist 'head' shops, at some festivals, dance events or by herbalists.	Ephedrine has stimulant effects similar to higher doses of caffeine, causing cold hands and feet, spinal shivers and light headedness. Muscle spasm and nausea are also possible. Yohimbe is reported to act as an aphrodisiac, with stimulant properties such as raised blood pressure, dizziness, and at high doses hallucinations. Salvia is more hallucinogenic and acts as a stimulant.

Drugs that alter perceptual function

Drug group	Principal drugs		Legal status
	Scientific names	*Trade, slang & other names*	
LSD	lysergic acid diethylamide and lysergide	LSD, 'acid' 'tabs' 'trips'	Controlled drugs; LSD not available for medical use.
HALLUCINOGENIC MUSHROOMS	psilocybe semilanceata (contains psilocybin and psilocin)	Liberty Cap, 'magic mushrooms' 'mushies'	If prepared for use may be a controlled drug. Otherwise unrestricted.
	Amanita muscaria	Fly Agaric	
CANNABIS	CANNABIS SATIVA (contains tetrahydrocannabinol)	'Pot', 'dope', 'blow', 'draw', 'smoke', 'puff' etc	Controlled drugs; not yet available for medical use; illegal to allow premises to be used for smoking cannabis.
	Herbal cannabis	'grass', 'marihuana', 'ganja', 'weed', 'the herb', 'skunk' etc.	
	Cannabis resin Cannabis oil	'hash', 'hashish'	
DMT	N,N-dimethyltryptamine	DMT, business man's lunch	Controlled drug, not available for medical use.
KETAMINE	Ketamine, Ketalar	Ketamine, Special K	Prescription only medicine. Not controlled under the Misuse of Drugs Act.

Drug group tables

Recommended medical uses	Methods of administration	Prevalence and availability	Effects
None.	Swallowed as variously formed, illicitly produced paper squares, pills, tablets, capsules, etc.	Illicitly manufactured LSD is commonly available on the illicit market.	Heightened appreciation of sensory experiences, perceptual distortions, feelings of dissociation, insight, elevation of mood. Sometimes anxiety or panic, occasionally severe. Relatively little physiological arousal or sedation, and minimal risk of physical dependence. With hallucinogens and hallucinogenic mushrooms, commonly pseudohallucinations. With cannabis, relaxation, drowsiness, talkativeness.
None.	Swallowed raw, cooked or brewed into a beverage, often after drying.	Liberty Caps grow wild in autumn in many parts of Britain and are commonly taken for hallucinogenic effects. Use of other mushrooms rare.	
None.	Burnt and smoked by itself (herbal cannabis) or with tobacco. Sometimes eaten (resin).	Most widely misused controlled drug in Britain. Probably five million people in UK use cannabis. Smuggled supplies widely available on illicit market.	
None.	Snorted or swallowed, usually smoked.	Illicitly manufactured in UK, more often imported. Limited availability.	A strong hallucinogen producing a short lived (30–60 minutes if smoked or snorted) intense state of intoxication. Users may appear very intoxicated during this episode, experiencing intense, introspective hallucinations. Because of the rapid onset of these effects, users may feel very disoriented or anxious.
Used by vets as anaesthetic, and to a lesser extent similarly with individuals, such as the elderly and children, less prone to adverse side effects.	Swallowed or snorted as pills or powder. Solution form can be injected.	Supplies generally diverted from medical supplies and sold as ketamine powder or pills, or falsely as ecstasy. This drug tends therefore to be available in similar events as ecstasy, though to a lesser extent.	When swallowed effects such as exhilaration, nausea, numbness, visual distortions and dissociation can occur, with the user feeling they are floating outside of the body. With strong doses hallucinations similar to LSD have been reported. Users may also experience discomfort, anxiety, confusion, muscle spasms and paranoia. At higher doses unconsciousness can occur. The inability to feel, and therefore avoid pain, may result in injury.

DrugScope membership

With direct access to decision makers and MPs, and
regular representation in print, broadcast and online
media, DrugScope is in a position to make a substantial
contribution to policy-making on drug-related matters.
As well as making use of our own in-house expertise,
our policy work draws on the knowledge and experience
of our 1,200 members, ensuring that the voices of
professionals from across the drugs field are heard.

As a DrugScope member you will benefit from:

- access to sound, up-to-date information on research
  findings and developments in the field, through the
  exclusive Members Briefing;

- sharing information and discussing specific policy
  issues, in members-only forums and seminars;

- free subscription to *Druglink*, the UK's only magazine
  dedicated to drug policy;

- reduced delegate rates for DrugScope's wide range
  of conferences and seminars;

- online information on our members' website;

- discounted access to the UK's pre-eminent library
  and information service on drug-related issues; and,

- the opportunity to play a part in a dynamic
  community of organisations and individuals, all
  working to influence UK drug policy and improve
  the standards of drug services.

To find out more about DrugScope's membership
scheme you can:

- visit the membership pages on the DrugScope
  website – www.drugscope.org.uk;

- e-mail membership@drugscope.org.uk; or

- call 0870 774 3684 and ask for a membership pack.

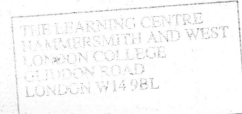